D1475990

Phase Locked Loops

Microwave Technology Series

The *Microwave Technology Series* publishes authoritative works for professional engineers, researchers and advanced students across the entire range of microwave devices, sub-systems, systems and applications. The series aims to meet the reader's needs for relevant information useful in practical applications. Engineers involved in microwave devices and circuits, antennas, broadcasting communications, radar, infra-red and avionics will find the series an invaluable source of design and reference information.

Series editors:
Michel-Henri Carpentier
Professor in 'Grandes Écoles', France,
Fellow of the IEEE, and President of the French SEE

Bradford L. Smith
International Patents Consultant and Engineer
with the Alcatel group in Paris, France,
and a Senior Member of the IEEE and French SEE

Phase Locked Loops

J. B. Encinas

Institut Supérieur d'Electronique
de Paris, France

CHAPMAN & HALL
London · Glasgow · New York · Tokyo · Melbourne · Madras

Published by Chapman & Hall, 2–6 Boundary Row, London SE1 8HN

Chapman & Hall, 2–6 Boundary Row, London SE1 8HN, UK

Blackie Academic & Professional, Wester Cleddens Road, Bishopbriggs, Glasgow G64 2NZ, UK

Chapman & Hall Inc., 29 West 35th Street, New York NY 10001, USA

Chapman & Hall, Japan, Thomson Publishing Japan, Hirakawacho Nemoto Building, 6F, 1-7-11 Hirakawa-cho, Chiyoda-ku, Tokyo 102, Japan

Chapman & Hall Australia, Thomas Nelson Australia, 102 Dodds Street, South Melbourne, Victoria 3205, Australia

Chapman & Hall India, R. Seshadri, 32 Second Main Road, CIT East, Madras 600 035, India

English language edition 1993

© 1993 Chapman & Hall

Original French language edition – Systèmes à verrouillage de phase (P.L.L.)– © 1989, Masson, Paris.

Typeset in 10/12 Times by Thomson Press (India) Ltd, New Delhi
Printed in Great Britain by St. Edmundsbury Press, Bury St. Edmunds, Suffolk

ISBN 0 412 48260 6

A Catalogue record for this book is available from the British Library

Encinas, J.B.
    Phase locked loops / J.B. Encinas.—English language ed.
      p.   cm.—(Microwave technology series)
    Translated from the French.
    Includes index.
    ISBN 0-412-48260-6 (acid-free)
    1. Phase-locked loops. I. Title. II. Series.
TK7872.P38E53   1993
621.381′3—dc20

92-38973
CIP

Contents

Preface

This book is devoted to a detailed and comprehensive study of phase locked loops aimed at preparing the reader to design them and to understand their applications. It is written at a level corresponding to a final year electronics undergraduate or a postgraduate student.

Linear and semidigital phase locked loops are studied in nine chapters. Most of this book is concerned with analogue PLLs, but there are chapters on semidigital PLLs and on applications. The mathematical tools and background required are described at the end of the book.

Important symbols

A	Amplifier gain
A	Mixer gain (V^{-1})
B_i	Filter bandwidth (Hz)
B_L	Low pass filter bandwidth (Hz)
B_n	Unilateral equivalent noise bandwidth (Hz)
$D(s)$	Polynomial of variable s
E_e	Peak amplitude of signal voltage (V)
E_r	Peak amplitude of reference signal voltage (V)
f_c	Carrier frequency (Hz)
f_i	Intermediate frequency (Hz)
f_{IF}	Intermediate frequency (Hz)
f_l	Local oscillator frequency (Hz)
f_r	Reference frequency (Hz)
$F(s)$	Transfer function of loop filter
G	Amplifier voltage gain
k_m	FM modulator sensitivity $(\text{rad s}^{-1}\,\text{V}^{-1})$
K	Motor coefficient (rad s^{-1})
K_1	Back-electromotive force coefficient (V s rad^{-1})
K_e	Reverse back-electromotive force coefficient $(\text{rad V}^{-1}\,\text{s}^{-1})$
K_d	PC conversion gain (V rad s^{-1})
K_M	Motor torque coefficient (N m A^{-1})
K_0	VCO conversion gain $(\text{rad s}^{-1}\,\text{V}^{-1})$
K_v	Conversion gain of PLL (s^{-2})
m	Modulation factor
m	Integer
n	Integer
n	Loop order
N_1, N_2	Integers representing division
N_0	Power spectral density (W Hz^{-1})
$N(s)$	Polynomial of variable s
P	Integer representing division
P_{nr}	Noise power of reference signal (W)
P_{sr}	Reference signal power (W)
$s = \sigma + j\omega$	Laplace transform variable

$\lvert SNR \rvert_r$	Signal-to-noise ratio at the input
$\lvert SNR \rvert_l$	Signal-to-noise ratio at the loop
t	Time (s)
T_0	Motor time constant (s)
T_0	Local oscillator (or VCO) period (s)
$T(s)$	Closed-loop transfer function
$T'(s)$	Open-loop transfer function
T_l	Lock in time (s)
T_m	Motor time constant (s)
T_P	Pull in time (s)
v_f	Filter output voltage (V)
v_d	PC output voltage (V)
v_c	Peak amplitude of carrier signal (V)
$V_f(s)$	Laplace transform of filter output voltage
v_m	Peak amplitude of modulating signal voltage (V)
α	Routh's table coefficient
$\theta_{1n}(t)$	Phase excitation signal (rad)
θ_e	Loop phase error (rad)
θ_1	Phase of VCO signal (rad)
θ_r	Phase of reference signal (rad)
$\theta_{11}(t)$	Phase step excitation
$\theta_{12}(t)$	Angular frequency step excitation
$\theta_{13}(t)$	Angular frequency ramp excitation
$\Delta\theta$	Amplitude of phase step (rad)
ζ	Damping factor
τ	Time constant (s)
τ_1, τ_2, τ_3	Time constants in loop filter (s)
$\Delta\phi$	Amplitude of phase step excitation signal (rad)
ϕ_M	Phase margin (rad)
ω	Angular frequency (rad s^{-1})
$j\omega$	Fourier transform variable (rad s^{-1})
ω_1	Angular frequency of output VCO signal (rad s^{-1})
ω_0	Running angular frequency of VCO signal (rad s^{-1})
ω_0	Centre angular frequency (rad s^{-1})
ω_r	Angular frequency of reference signal (rad s^{-1})
ω_m	Modulating angular frequency (rad s^{-1})
ω_n	Natural angular frequency (rad s^{-1})
ω_1	Cut-off angular frequency (rad)
ω_{-3dB}	Corner angular frequency (rad)
$\Delta\omega$	Amplitude of angular frequency step (rad s^{-1})
$\Delta\dot\omega$	Rate of change of frequency (rad s^{-1})
$\pm\Delta\omega_H$	Hold range (rad s^{-1})
$\pm\Delta\omega_L$	Lock in range (rad s^{-1})
$\pm\Delta\omega_P$	Pull in range (rad s^{-1})
$\pm\Delta\omega_{PO}$	Pull out range (rad s^{-1})

Abbreviations

AM	Amplitude modulation
DC	Direct current
DSB–SC	Double-sideband suppressed carrier
FM	Frequency modulation
FSK	Fast shift keying
IF	Intermediate frequency
LO	Local oscillator
LPF	Low pass filter
PC	Phase comparator
PLL	Phase locked loop
RF	Radio frequency
SSB–SC	Single-sideband suppressed carrier
VCO	Voltage controlled oscillator

1

Simplified operation of PLL circuits

1.1 PLL CIRCUITS

1.1.1 Purpose

A PLL is a circuit which synchronizes the frequency of the output signal gener-
ated by an oscillator with the frequency of a reference signal by means of the
phase difference of the two signals.

1.1.2 Block diagram

The system consists of three basic blocks (Fig. 1.1).

1. *Phase comparator (PC)*. A simple one can be realized by means of an analogue multiplier. Since the circuit performs a multiplication the output signal
   v_d will have the following form:

$$v_d = K_d f(\phi_r - \phi_l)$$

   where f is a function of the phase difference between the reference and the
   oscillator signals and K_d is the conversion gain of the PC expressed in units of
   volts per radian.
2. *Low pass filter (LPF)*. For simplicity the filter is supposed perfect. The output
   voltage will be denoted by v_f.
3. *Voltage controlled oscillator (VCO)*. The output filter voltage v_f controls

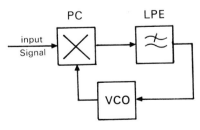

Fig. 1.1 Block diagram of a PLL.

the VCO angular frequency according to the following transfer character-istic:

$$\omega_1 = \omega_0 + K_0 v_f \tag{1.1}$$

where ω_0 is the running angular frequency, corresponding to $v_f = 0$, and K_0 the VCO conversion gain which can be expressed in units of radians per second per volt or hertz per volt.

1.2   OPERATION PRINCIPLE

1.2.1   Synchronized or locked state

When the circuit operates in the locked state the angular frequency of the reference signal and the angular frequency of the VCO output signal are equal.

Let the following expressions represent, respectively, the reference and VCO signals:

$$r(t) = E_r \cos(\omega_r t + \phi_r)$$
$$l(t) = E_1 \cos(\omega_1 t + \phi_1)$$

As the PC performs a multiplication its output will provide $v_d(t) = \beta r(t) l(t) = K_d \{\cos[(\omega_r - \omega_1)t + \phi_r - \phi_1] + \cos[(\omega_r + \omega_1)t + \phi_r + \phi_1]\}$ where β is a constant. After filtering we obtain

$$v_f(t) = K_d \cos[(\omega_r - \omega_1)t + \phi_r - \phi_1]$$
$$K_d = \beta \frac{E_r E_1}{2}$$

To start with, no voltage v_f is applied at the input of the VCO. Thus $\omega_1 = \omega_0$.

Let us represent $v_f(t)$ by the projection along the horizontal axis of a vector named $\overrightarrow{OH}$ whose magnitude is K_d, which rotates with an angular frequency of $\omega_r - \omega_0$ (Fig. 1.2). The angle from $\overrightarrow{OH}$ to the horizontal axis represents the phase difference, at any time, of the reference signal and the VCO output signal. The reference signal is represented by a motionless vector $\overrightarrow{OG}$ whose magnitude will arbitrarily be the same as $\overrightarrow{OH}$, that is to say K_d.

The positive rotation direction is clockwise and indicated by an arrow. Let us suppose $\omega_r - \omega_0 > 0$; therefore, $\overrightarrow{OH}$, which represents the VCO output signal, rotates clockwise. On the other hand, $\overrightarrow{OG}$, which represents the reference signal, will remain motionless.

As the filter has been supposed perfect the projection of $\overrightarrow{OH}$ along the horizontal axis represents v_f and controls the VCO angular frequency when it is applied at its input.

Although represented in a stationary position $\overrightarrow{OG}$, in reality it rotates with an angular frequency ω_r. Nevertheless, if we use a synchronized strobe light it will 'freeze' $\overrightarrow{OG}$ and it will appear stationary.

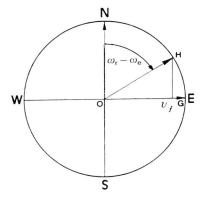

Fig. 1.2 Illustration of a PLL.

Let t be the time at which v_f is applied at the VCO input. Its range will extend from $+K_d$ to $-K_d$ which are the limits of the $\overrightarrow{OH}$ projection along the horizontal axis. Therefore, the VCO angular frequency will remain within the following limits:

$$\omega_M = \omega_0 + K_0 K_d$$
$$\omega_m = \omega_0 - K_0 K_d$$

When the angular reference frequency remains between ω_m and ω_M there exists an angular frequency of the VCO ω_1 equal to ω_r. Such a condition occurs when $\overrightarrow{OH}$ becomes motionless; its horizontal projection will then fulfil the double condition

$$v_f = \frac{\omega_1 - \omega_0}{K_0} = \frac{\omega_r - \omega_0}{K_0}$$

If the point H is stable the locked state will remain stable. Let us suppose, for instance, that a random signal decreases the VCO angular frequency by an amount $\Delta\omega$. The point H will rotate to the right, reaching a new position H'. The $\overrightarrow{OH}$ projection will then increase by Δv_f and the VCO will be controlled by $v_f + \Delta v_f$ and therefore the VCO angular frequency will increase, inhibiting the action of the disturbance. The result will be

$$\Delta\omega_1 = K_0 \Delta v_f$$

Thus, as soon as the VCO angular frequency is driven apart from the reference one, by some random signal, by temperature variation or by another means, a phase error will result generating a voltage which will force the VCO to synchronize with the reference angular frequency (Fig. 1.3).

If the reference angular frequency equals the running frequency ω_0 of the VCO $v_f = 0$ the point H is at noon on the diagram. The angle from $\overrightarrow{OH}$ to $\overrightarrow{OG}$ is then $\pi/2$. This situation will last as long as $\omega_r = \omega_0$.

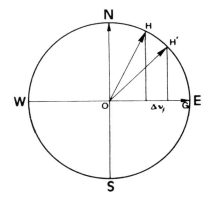

Fig. 1.3   Illustration of the action of a PLL.

In order to be compatible with PLL literature we shall define the phase error as the angle θ_e from $\overrightarrow{OH}$ to the vertical axis (Fig. 1.4).

Then we have

$$v_f = K_d \cos\left(\frac{\pi}{2} - \theta_e\right)$$

$$= K_d \sin \theta_e \tag{1.2}$$

With this definition the phase error is zero when the reference angular frequency equals the running VCO angular frequency.

Let $\Delta\theta_e$ be a small error; then

$$\Delta v_f = K_d \Delta\theta_e$$

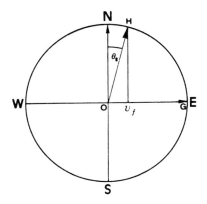

Fig. 1.4   Phase error.

and (equation (1.1))

$$\Delta v_f = \frac{\Delta \omega}{K_0}$$

then we obtain

$$\Delta \theta_e = \frac{\Delta \omega}{K_d K_0}$$

This phase error forces the VCO to shift its angular frequency which becomes identical to the reference one.

1.2.2 Sinusoidal response

The geometric representation of the PLL action gives a simple picture of the frequency demodulation.

Let the following expression represent a frequency modulated signal

$$e(t) = E_e \cos \left(\omega_0 t + \frac{\Delta \omega}{\omega_m} \sin \omega_m t \right) \tag{1.3}$$

The derivative of the phase is

$$\omega_r = \omega_0 + \Delta \omega \cos \omega_m t \tag{1.4}$$

From equations (1.1) and (1.4) and if the circuit is locked, then $\omega_r = \omega_1$ and we obtain

$$v_f = \frac{\omega_1 - \omega_0}{K_0} = \frac{\Delta \omega}{K_0} \cos \omega_m t \tag{1.5}$$

Figure 1.4 allows us to calculate

$$\frac{v_f}{K_d} = \sin \theta_e \approx \theta_e \tag{1.6}$$

and

$$\theta_e \approx \frac{\Delta \omega}{K_d K_0} \cos \omega_m t \tag{1.7}$$

The PC used until now, by the nature of its characteristic is of the sinusoidal type. In FM (Fig. 1.5), in order to work in the linear zone the phase will be limited to $\theta_e < \pi/6$, and therefore

$$\frac{\Delta \omega}{K_d K_0} < 0.5$$

The point H will then describe the arc corresponding to the variation of the phase error given by equation (1.7). The demodulated voltage is represented by

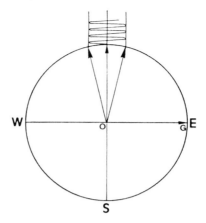

Fig. 1.5   Representation of FM demodulation.

equation (1.5), that is to say

$$v_f = \frac{\Delta\omega}{K_0} \cos \omega_m t$$

1.2.3   Transient response

(a)   Phase step

The reference signal exhibits a phase step as represented in Fig. 1.6 where the point H has shifted, momentarily, to H', the reference angular frequency remaining the same.

The phase step is converted into a voltage step by the PC and then filtered; thus

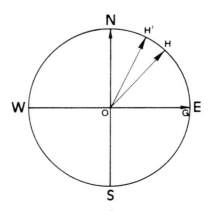

Fig. 1.6   Rotation of $\overrightarrow{OH}$ due to the phase step.

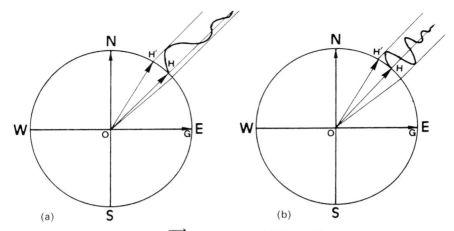

Fig. 1.7 $\overrightarrow{OH}$ returns to its initial position.

the VCO angular frequency will be shifted. As the reference angular frequency remains constant the VCO angular frequency will return to its initial value. Figure 1.7 illustrates its return. According to the LPF time constant the return to its initial position will be more or less long.

(b)   Reference angular frequency step

The reference angular frequency exhibits a step from ω_r to $\omega_r + \Delta\omega$.

As can be seen in Fig. 1.8 $\overrightarrow{OH}$ will be shifted to a new equilibrium position that will take a certain time related to the damping of the circuit. Figure 1.8(a) corresponds to a very damped system and Fig. 1.8(b) to an underdamped system.

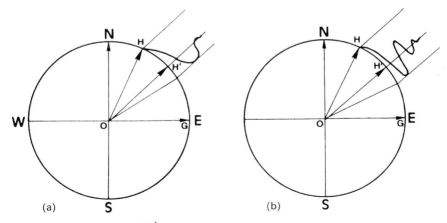

Fig. 1.8 $\overrightarrow{OH}$ returns to its new equilibrium position.

Notice that if the reference angular frequency is large enough, so that $\overrightarrow{OH}$ reaches a horizontal position, the system unlocks.

1.2.4   Hold range

This is the angular frequency range, defined by $2\,|\triangle\omega_H|$, over which the PLL remains in lock. It is referred to as either the hold range or the tracking range.

From equations (1.1) and (1.2) we can eliminate v_f and we obtain

$$\sin\theta_e = \frac{\omega_1 - \omega_0}{K_d K_0}$$

but, since $-1 \leqslant \sin\theta_e \leqslant 1$, the following condition prevails:

$$\frac{|\omega_H - \omega_0|}{K_d K_0} = 1$$

$\omega_0 \pm \omega_H$ being the limits within which the tracking is maintained. Thus

$$|\omega_H - \omega_0| = K_d K_0$$
$$|\triangle\omega_H| = K_d K_0$$

Therefore, the hold range is

$$2\,|\triangle\omega_H| = 2K_d K_0 \qquad (1.8)$$

and the reference angular frequency ω_r must fulfil the following double inequality:

$$\omega_0 - K_d K_0 \leqslant \omega_r \leqslant \omega_0 + K_d K_0$$

1.2.5   Capture range

This is the angular frequency range over which a PLL, if unlocked, will be able to acquire lock.

In order to determine it let us suppose that the PLL is unlocked, that the LPF is perfect and that

$$\omega_r < \omega_0 - K_d K_0$$

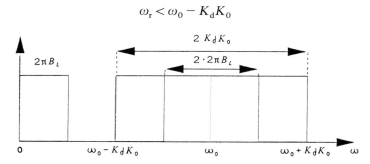

Fig. 1.9   LPF spectrum and VCO angular frequency range.

If the low pass bandwidth is B_L then we have

$$2\pi B_L < K_d K_0$$

Figure 1.9 represents the spectrum of LPF and the angular frequency range of the VCO.

If the reference angular frequency is progressively increased from a value inferior to $\omega_0 - K_d K_0$ the lock will occur if

$$\omega_r - \omega_0 \leqslant 2\pi B_L = \Delta\omega_L$$

If ω_r continues to increase the lock will be maintained until ω_r reaches the limit $\omega_0 + |\Delta\omega_H| = \omega_0 + K_d K_0$.

In the same manner, if ω_r is decreased from a value lower than $\omega_0 + K_d K_0$ capture will occur when

$$\omega_r - \omega_0 < |\Delta\omega_L|$$

Lock will be maintained until ω_r reaches the limit

$$\omega_0 - |\Delta\omega_H|$$

Therefore, the capture range is

$$2|\Delta\omega_L| = 2 \times 2\pi B_L \qquad (1.9)$$

The schematic of Fig. 1.10 represents the hold range and the capture range.

1.2.6 Noise

If a noise signal is added to a reference sinusoidal signal, the zero crossings will be displaced back or forward but its angular frequency will remain constant (Fig. 1.11).

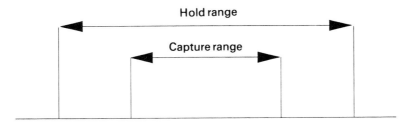

Fig. 1.10 Hold and capture ranges.

Fig. 1.11 Random displacements of the reference signal.

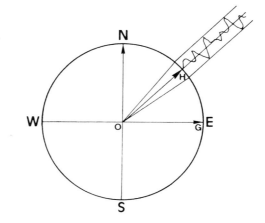

Fig. 1.12   Illustration of noise.

Phase steps will result in a random manner and $\overrightarrow{\mathrm{OH}}$ will jitter around its equilibrium position as illustrated in Fig. 1.12.

1.2.7   Exercise

A sinusoidal PC has a maximum 2 V range. What is the value of its conversion gain K_d? It is used in a PLL whose VCO has a running frequency of 5×10^3 Hz. Its conversion gain K_0 is $2\pi \times 100$ rad s^{-1} V^{-1}. Calculate the hold range in hertz.

Solution   The value of K_d is 2 V rad^{-1}. The hold range is determined from equation (1.8); we obtain $2 \times 2\pi\ 100 = 1256.6$ rad s^{-1} and in hertz ± 200

$$4800 \leqslant f_f \leqslant 5200$$

2

Analysis methods for linear PLLs

The main blocks of the PLL were shown in Chapter 1. The operation of the PLL was studied in an elementary way, with the help of the trigonometric circle, which allowed us to determine its main characteristics, and among them the hold range.

In this chapter the analysis techniques needed to design and to calculate the elements of a PLL circuit will be developed and the conditions regarding the validity of the results will be thoroughly examined.

The functional characteristics of the PC, the LPF and the VCO will be studied. Then we shall determine the transfer function of each filter from which we shall be able to study the stability of the PLL.

2.1 INTRODUCTION

2.1.1 Validity conditions

All the results that follow are based upon the assumption that the systems are linear. This means that the output signals must be related to the input signals by a system of linear differential equations. Although the physical systems are never fully linear we can consider them as such, as long as the magnitudes of the signals applied to their inputs are within certain limits.

2.1.2 Determination of the functional diagram in the frequency domain

In Chapter 1 was described the functional diagram (see Fig. 1.1) as it appears in reality, that is to say in the time domain. That is why the applied signals were time dependent. As it is much easier to derive the results in the frequency domain we are going to transform the time block diagram in a frequency block diagram.

In order to do that, a very simple case will be considered and its results will be generalized.

Let us consider the filter illustrated in Fig. 2.1. According to Ohm's law we have

$$v_d(t) = RC \frac{dv_f(t)}{dt} + v_f(t) \tag{2.1}$$

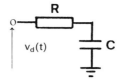

Fig. 2.1   *RC* filter: type 1.

By integration of equation (1.1), we obtain

$$\omega_1(t)t = \omega_0 t + K_0 \int_0^t v_f(t)\,dt \tag{2.2}$$

Thus

$$\theta_1(t) = K_0 \int_0^t v_f(t)\,dt \tag{2.3}$$

and differentiating

$$\frac{d\theta_1(t)}{dt} = K_0 v_f(t) \tag{2.4}$$

$$\frac{d^2\theta_1(t)}{dt^2} = K_0 \frac{dv_f(t)}{dt} \tag{2.5}$$

The combination of equation (2.1) and equations (2.4) and (2.5) gives the following second-order differential equation:

$$\frac{RC}{K_0}\frac{d^2\theta_1(t)}{dt^2} + \frac{1}{K_0}\frac{d\theta_1(t)}{dt} = v_d(t) \tag{2.6}$$

However, we have

$$v_d(t) = K_d \theta_e(t) = K_d[\theta_r(t) - \theta_1(t)] \tag{2.7}$$

Setting $RC = \tau$ and using equations (2.6) and (2.7), we deduce

$$\frac{d^2\theta_1(t)}{dt^2} + \frac{1}{\tau}\frac{d\theta_1(t)}{dt} + \frac{K_d K_0}{\tau}\theta_1(t) = \frac{K_d K_0}{\tau}\theta_r(t) \tag{2.8}$$

which is a second-order differential equation whose coefficients are constant. Therefore, the Laplace transform can be taken and we find

$$s^2\Theta_1(s) + \frac{1}{\tau}s\Theta_1(s) + \frac{K_d K_0}{\tau}\Theta_1(s) = \frac{K_d K_0}{\tau}\Theta_r(s) \tag{2.9}$$

from which we obtain, setting $K_d K_0 = K_v$ (in reciprocal seconds)

$$\frac{\Theta_1(s)}{\Theta_r(s)} = \frac{K_v/\tau}{s^2 + s/\tau + K_v/\tau} \tag{2.10}$$

Using the relationship

$$\Theta_e(s) = \Theta_r(s) - \Theta_1(s) \tag{2.11}$$

and combining it with equation (2.10) and replacing $1/(s\tau + 1)$ with $F(s)$, we obtain

$$\frac{\Theta_1(s)}{\Theta_e(s)} = \frac{K_v}{s} \frac{1}{s\tau + 1} \tag{2.12}$$

$$= K_v \frac{F(s)}{s} \tag{2.13}$$

Equation (2.13) can be generalized and it can be applied to any type of filter whose transfer function is $F(s)$.

From equations (2.11) and (2.13) it is possible to obtain the functional diagram in the frequency domain (Fig. 2.2). One can see, immediately, the correspondence between the time domain and the frequency domain:

$$v_d(t) = K_d[\theta_r(t) - \theta_1(t)] \rightarrow V_d(s) = K_d[\Theta_r(s) - \Theta_1(s)]$$

$$v_f(t) = \frac{\omega_1(t) - \omega_0}{K_0} \rightarrow V_f(s) = \frac{\Theta_1(s)}{K_0}s$$

We could expect to obtain such a result since the Laplace transformation of equation (2.3) is

$$\Theta_1(s) = K_0 \frac{V_f(s)}{s}$$

That is to say,

$$V_f(s) = \frac{\Theta_1(s)}{K_0}s \tag{2.14}$$

It is worthwhile obtaining a relationship between $V_f(s)$ and $\Theta_r(s)$. With the elimination of Θ_1 between equations (2.10) and (2.14), and using the expression $1/(s\tau + 1) = F(s)$, we deduce such a relationship:

$$\frac{V_f(s)}{\Theta_r(s)} = \frac{sK_dF(s)}{s + K_vF(s)} \tag{2.15}$$

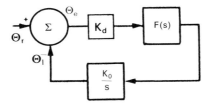

Fig. 2.2   Functional diagram in the frequency domain.

Taking into account the definitions of feedback systems the transfer function of the open-loop gain is

$$T'(s) = \frac{K_v F(s)}{s} \qquad (2.16)$$

and of the closed-loop gain

$$T(s) = \frac{K_v F(s)}{s + K_v F(s)} \qquad (2.17)$$

Therefore, we can write equation (2.15) as follows:

$$\frac{V_f(s)}{\Theta_r(s)} = \frac{s}{K_0} T(s) \qquad (2.18)$$

Remark. If an amplifier, having a gain of A, were present between the PC and LPF, the loop gain would be AK_v. In order not to change the expressions used until now the amplifier gain is included in the expression K_v. We shall see, later in this chapter, how operational amplifiers are used in combination with filters.

2.1.3   Loop order

The loop order is given by the degree of the denominator of the polynomial of the closed-loop transfer function.

The denominator of the transfer function equation of a PLL is, according to equation (2.17), as follows:

$$s + K_v F(s)$$

Let

$$F(s) = \frac{N(s)}{D(s)}$$

be the general form of the filter transfer function where $N(s)$ and $D(s)$ are two polynomials whose degrees are respectively m and n with the condition $n \geqslant m$.

Let us insert the above equation into equation (2.17); we then have

$$T(s) = \frac{K_v N(s)}{s D(s) + K_v N(s)}$$

The degree of the denominator is the degree of $sD(s)$.

Thus, it can be stated that the order of a PLL system is equal to the order of the filter plus 1.

2.2 IDEALIZED CHARACTERISTICS OF PLL ELEMENTS

2.2.1 Phase comparator

In Chapter 1 we used an analogue PC of the sinusoidal type whose characteristic is

$$v_d = K_d \sin \theta_e$$

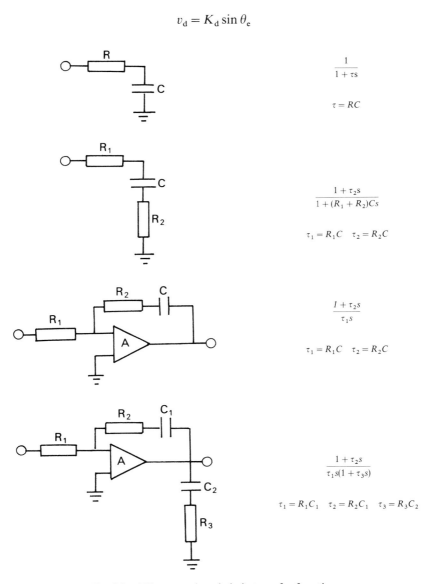

$$\frac{1}{1 + \tau s}$$

$$\tau = RC$$

$$\frac{1 + \tau_2 s}{1 + (R_1 + R_2)Cs}$$

$$\tau_1 = R_1 C \quad \tau_2 = R_2 C$$

$$\frac{1 + \tau_2 s}{\tau_1 s}$$

$$\tau_1 = R_1 C \quad \tau_2 = R_2 C$$

$$\frac{1 + \tau_2 s}{\tau_1 s(1 + \tau_3 s)}$$

$$\tau_1 = R_1 C_1 \quad \tau_2 = R_2 C_1 \quad \tau_3 = R_3 C_2$$

Fig. 2.3 Filters used and their transfer functions.

In order to obtain linear equations we must get rid of the sine term. This can be done if the angle θ_e is small enough so that

$$\sin \theta_e \approx \theta_e$$

The characteristic of the PC is then

$$v_d = K_d \theta_e$$

2.2.2   Low pass filters

Figure 2.3 illustrates the different types of filters used in this book together with their transfer function.

2.2.3   Voltage controlled oscillator

The frequency of its output signal is controlled by the output voltage of the LPF. We have already seen its characteristic

$$\omega_1 = \omega_0 + K_0 v_f$$

Owing to the fact that the VCO is driven by a voltage which cannot exceed K_d in magnitude and that the VCO can be driven by higher voltages, an amplifier follows the PC. When active filters are used the output signal of the PC is also amplified as will be seen in this chapter.

2.3   FIRST-ORDER LOOP

This corresponds to the case where $F(s) = 1$, that is to say when there is no filter. Actually, the transfer function order of the filter being 0, that of the loop is 1.

According to equation (2.17), the first-order closed-loop transfer function is

$$T(s) = \frac{K_v}{s + K_v}$$

and the open-loop transfer is obtained from equation (2.16):

$$T'(s) = \frac{K_v}{s}$$

2.3.1   Stability determined by Evans' method

Let us reconsider the closed-loop transfer function. Setting

$$K_v = \omega_n$$

we find

$$T(s) = \frac{K_v}{s + K_v} = \frac{\omega_n}{s + \omega_n}$$

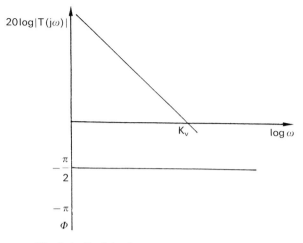

Fig. 2.4   Bode's diagram: first-order system.

From the characteristic equation

$$s + \omega_n = 0$$

the root is equal to $-\omega_n$. Because the root is negative the system is unconditionally stable. The Evans root locus is reduced to a point.

2.3.2   Stability determined by Bode's method

The open-loop transfer function is

$$T'(s) = \frac{\omega_n}{s}$$

Therefore, we have

$$|T(j\omega)| = \frac{\omega_n}{\omega}$$

$$\Phi = -90°$$

and the Bode diagram can be drawn (Fig. 2.4).

In this particular case the curve representing $20 \log|T'(j\omega)|$ is a straight line which crosses the angular frequency axis in a point where the magnitude of the open-loop transfer function equals 1. On the other hand, the phase, being constant, is represented by a straight line parallel to the angular frequency axis.

The frequency $\omega_1/2\pi$, the cut-off frequency for which $|T'(j\omega_n)| = 1$, corresponds to $\omega_n/2\pi$.

Since for such an angular frequency the phase is equal to $-90°$, the system is thus unconditionally stable.

2.4   SECOND-ORDER LOOPS

Three types of filters will be studied: two are of the passive type and one of the active type (see Fig. 2.3).

We are going to determine in each case the closed-loop and open-loop transfer function and the stability from Evans's and Bode's methods.

2.4.1   Low pass filter with no zeros and a single pole

(a)   Closed-loop transfer function

The transfer function of the filter is given by the expression

$$F(s) = \frac{1}{s\tau + 1} \tag{2.19}$$

This filter has already been studied to obtain the functional block diagram in the frequency domain (Fig. 2.2). The transfer function of the system was also determined; see equation (2.10).

By analogy with some mechanical systems it is common practice to set

$$2\omega_n \zeta = \frac{1}{\tau} \tag{2.20a}$$

$$\omega_n^2 = \frac{K_v}{\tau} \tag{2.20b}$$

where ω_n is called the natural angular frequency and ζ the damping factor. Equation (2.10) is then re-written as follows

$$T(s) = \frac{\Theta_1(s)}{\Theta_r(s)} = \frac{\omega_n^2}{s^2 + 2\zeta\omega_n s + \omega_n^2} \tag{2.21}$$

(b)   Open-loop transfer function

This is given by equation (2.13), where we shall replace $F(s)$ with $1/(s\tau + 1)$. We obtain

$$T'(s) = \frac{K_v}{s(s\tau + 1)} \tag{2.22}$$

(c)   Stability determined by Evans' method

We must solve for the two roots of the characteristic equation

$$s^2 + 2\zeta\omega_n s + \omega_n^2 = 0$$

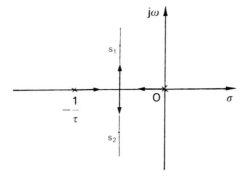

Fig. 2.5 Bode's pattern: type 1 filter.

When $\zeta^2 < 1$ the two poles are complex conjugates and we find

$$s_1, s_2 = -\omega_n[1 \pm j(1 - \zeta^2)^{1/2}]$$

Since their real term is always negative, the system is unconditionally stable.
In Fig. 2.5 the poles are represented in the complex s plane.

(d) Stability determined by Bode's method

The substitution of s with $j\omega$ in equation (2.22) gives

$$T'(j\omega) = \frac{K_v}{j\omega(1 + j\tau\omega)}$$

from which, we obtain

$$|T'(j\omega)| = \frac{K_v}{\omega(1 + \tau^2\omega^2)^{1/2}}$$

$$\tan \Phi = -\frac{1}{\tau\omega}$$

The angular frequency ω_1 at which

$$|T'(j\omega_1)| = 1$$

$$\frac{K_v}{\omega_1(1 + \tau^2\omega_1^2)^{1/2}} = 1$$

is defined as the cut-off angular frequency.
Let us square both sides of the above equation and rearrange its terms; we find

$$\tau^2\omega_1^4 + \omega_1^2 - K_v^2 = 0$$

and then, making use of equations (2.20a) and (2.20b), we obtain

$$\omega_1^4 + 4\zeta^2\omega_n^2\omega_1^2 - \omega_n^4 = 0$$

from which we deduce the cut-off angular frequency:

$$\omega_1 = \omega_n[(1 + 4\zeta^4)^{1/2} - 2\zeta^2]^{1/2} \tag{2.23}$$

Since $T'(j\omega)$ is out of phase by $-90°$ for $\omega = 0$, the phase Φ is given by the following expression:

$$\Phi = -\arctan\left(\frac{1}{\tau\omega_1}\right) - 90° = -\arctan\left(\frac{2\zeta\omega_n}{\omega_1}\right) - 90°$$

If ω_1 is replaced with equation (2.23), we have

$$\Phi = -\arctan\left\{\frac{2\zeta}{[(1 + 4\zeta^4)^{1/2} - 2\zeta^2]^{1/2}}\right\} - 90° \tag{2.24a}$$

It is worth noting that the phase is uniquely determined by the damping factor ζ, that is to say $1/2(K_v\tau)^{1/2}$. The stability increases when ζ increases and therefore when K_v and τ are small.

In order to ensure a phase margin of $45°$ the following equation has to be solved:

$$\frac{\pi}{4} = \frac{\pi}{2} - \arctan\left\{\frac{2\zeta}{[(1 + 4\zeta^4)^{1/2} - 2\zeta^2]^{1/2}}\right\}$$

$$1 = \frac{2\zeta}{[(1 + 4\zeta^4)^{1/2} - 2\zeta^2]^{1/2}}$$

We obtain $\zeta \geqslant 0.42$.

Figure 2.6 represents Bode's diagram: the magnitude and the phase of the open-loop transfer function.

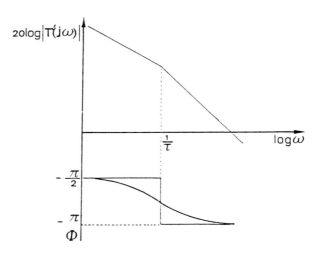

Fig. 2.6   Bode's diagram: type 1 filter.

(e) *Conclusions*

Although this filter is very simple it does not allow simultaneous optimization of bandwidth, damping factor and gain. For instance, it is not possible to reduce significantly the bandwidth without sacrificing the stability.

2.4.2 Low pass filter with one zero and a single pole

This filter is represented in Fig. 2.7.

(a) *Closed-loop transfer function*

Let us recall equation (2.17):

$$T(s) = \frac{K_v F(s)}{s + K_v F(s)}$$

The transfer function of the filter is

$$F(s) = \frac{1 + s\tau_2}{1 + s(\tau_1 + \tau_2)} \tag{2.24b}$$

Combining both, we find

$$T(s) = K_v \frac{(1 + s\tau_2)/(\tau_1 + \tau_2)}{s^2 + s(1 + K_v\tau_2)/(\tau_1 + \tau_2) + K_v/(\tau_1 + \tau_2)} \tag{2.25}$$

Setting

$$2\zeta\omega_n = \frac{1 + K_v\tau_2}{\tau_1 + \tau_2} \tag{2.26}$$

$$\omega_n = \left(\frac{K_v}{\tau_1 + \tau_2}\right)^{1/2} \tag{2.27}$$

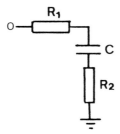

Fig. 2.7 Low pass filter with no zero and a single pole: type 2.

and substituting them into equation (2.25) yields

$$T(s) = \frac{(1 + s\tau_2)\omega_n^2}{s^2 + 2\zeta\omega_n s + \omega_n^2} \tag{2.28}$$

Let us calculate τ_2 as a function of ω_n and ζ. If equation (2.27) is squared, we obtain

$$\omega_n^2 = \frac{K_v}{\tau_1 + \tau_2} \tag{2.29}$$

The elimination of $\tau_1 + \tau_2$ between equation (2.26) and equation (2.29) gives

$$\frac{K_v}{\omega_n^2} = \frac{1 + K_v\tau_2}{2\zeta\omega_n} \tag{2.30}$$

from which we obtain

$$\tau_2 = \frac{1}{K_v}\left(\frac{2\zeta K_v}{\omega_n} - 1\right) \tag{2.31}$$

Substituting equation (2.31) into equation (2.28) gives

$$T(s) = \frac{\omega_n(2\zeta - \omega_n/K_v)s + \omega_n^2}{s^2 + 2\zeta\omega_n s + \omega_n^2} \tag{2.32}$$

(b)   Open-loop transfer function

Let us replace the expression of the filter transfer function into equation (2.16). We find

$$T'(s) = \frac{K_v}{s}\frac{1 + \tau_2 s}{1 + (\tau_1 + \tau_2)s} \tag{2.33}$$

(c)   Stability determined by Evans' method

From the characteristic equation

$$s^2 + \frac{1 + K_v\tau_2}{\tau_1 + \tau_2}s + \frac{K_v}{\tau_1 + \tau_2} = 0 \tag{2.34}$$

it is possible to determine the root locus diagram.

The Evans rules are given in Appendix A. Equation (2.33) which represents the open-loop transfer function will be used for this purpose. The fundamental characteristics of the root loci can be determined from this equation following the above procedure.

We can see that it has a zero $z = -1/\tau_2$ and two real poles $s = 0, s = -1/(\tau_1 + \tau_2)$.

1. *Loci starting points*. These are the poles of equation (2.33): $s = 0$, $s = -1/(\tau_1 + \tau_2)$.

2. *Loci termination point.* This is the zero $z = -1/\tau_2$.
3. *Root loci belonging to the real axis.* A point M belongs to the real axis if the total number of poles and zeros located to its right is an odd number.

It can be seen in Fig. 2.8, where we have marked the zero and the two poles of the open-loop transfer function, that the real root loci are situated on the left of the zero and between the two poles. They terminate on the zero where K_v reaches infinity.

4. *Points of departure of the root locus from real axis.* They depart as soon as the roots they represent become complex conjugates. Thus, the condition is

$$(1 + K_v\tau_2)^2 - 4K_v(\tau_1 + \tau_2) < 0$$

We also can determine the root loci from equation (2.34) which has the following solutions:

$$s_1 = -\frac{1}{2}\frac{1 + K_v\tau_2}{\tau_1 + \tau_2} + \frac{j}{2}\left[\frac{4K_v}{\tau_1 + \tau_2} - \left(\frac{1 + K_v\tau_2}{\tau_1 + \tau_2}\right)^2\right]^{1/2}$$

$$s_2 = -\frac{1}{2}\frac{1 + K_v\tau_2}{\tau_1 + \tau_2} - \frac{j}{2}\left[\frac{4K_v}{\tau_1 + \tau_2} - \left(\frac{1 + K_v\tau_2}{\tau_1 + \tau_2}\right)^2\right]^{1/2}$$

Setting

$$x = -\frac{1}{2}\frac{1 + K_v\tau_2}{\tau_1 + \tau_2} \tag{2.35}$$

$$y = \left(\frac{K_v}{\tau_1 + \tau_2} - x^2\right)^{1/2} \tag{2.36}$$

from equation (2.36) we obtain

$$x^2 + y^2 = \frac{K_v}{\tau_1 + \tau_2} \tag{2.37}$$

and from equation (2.35) we have

$$\frac{K_v}{\tau_1 + \tau_2} = \frac{-2}{\tau_2}\left[x + \frac{1}{2(\tau_1 + \tau_2)}\right] \tag{2.38}$$

Making use of equations (2.37) and (2.38) leads to

$$y^2 + \left(x + \frac{1}{\tau_2}\right)^2 = \frac{1}{\tau_2}\left(\frac{1}{\tau_2} - \frac{1}{\tau_1 + \tau_2}\right) \tag{2.39}$$

which is the equation of a circle whose centre has the coordinates $(-1/\tau_2, 0)$ and whose radius is

$$\left[\frac{1}{\tau_2}\left(\frac{1}{\tau_2} - \frac{1}{\tau_1 + \tau_2}\right)\right]^{1/2}$$

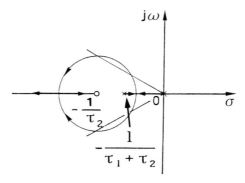

Fig. 2.8   Evans' locus: type 2 filter.

The radius of the circle being always $< 1/\tau_2$, the system is unconditionally stable.

Figure 2.8 represents Evans' root loci.

If from the origin two symmetrical straight semilines are drawn they define a constant damping factor. It can be seen that we can associate two values of K_v with them. Thus, a lower limit exists for the damping factor when the straight lines are tangent to the circle.

(d)   Stability determined by Bode's method

The open-loop transfer function is given by equation (2.33). Replacing s with $j\omega$, we obtain

$$T'(j\omega) = K_v \frac{1 + j\omega\tau_2}{j\omega[1 + j\omega(\tau_1 + \tau_2)]}$$

whose magnitude is

$$|T'(j\omega)| = \frac{K_v}{\omega}\left[\frac{1 + \omega^2\tau_2^2}{1 + \omega^2(\tau_1 + \tau_2)^2}\right]^{1/2} \tag{2.40}$$

and its phase is

$$\Phi = \arctan\omega\tau_2 - \arctan\omega(\tau_1 + \tau_2) - 90° \tag{2.41}$$

Let us determine the cut-off angular frequency ω_1, which can be obtained from $|T'(j\omega)| = 1$ after having squaring its two terms as follows:

$$\frac{K_v^2}{\omega_1^2}\frac{1 + \omega_1^2\tau_2^2}{1 + \omega_1^2(\tau_1 + \tau_2)^2} = 1$$

from which we obtain the equation

$$\omega_1^4 + \frac{1 - K_v^2\tau_2^2}{(\tau_1 + \tau_2)^2}\omega_1^2 - \frac{K_v^2}{(\tau_1 + \tau_2)^2} = 0$$

Only one solution satisfies the physical constraints:

$$\omega_1 = \left[\frac{1}{2(\tau_1 + \tau_2)^2} \{\tau_2^2 K_v^2 - 1 + [(1 - \tau_2^2 K_v^2)^2 + 4K_v^2(\tau_1 + \tau_2)^2]^{1/2}\} \right]^{1/2} \quad (2.42)$$

Let us replace $\tau_1 + \tau_2$ and τ_2 with their values obtained from equations (2.29) and (2.31) in the preceding expression; we obtain

$$\omega_1 = \frac{\omega_n^2}{K_v} \left\{ \frac{1}{2} \left[\left(2\zeta \frac{K_v}{\omega_n} - 1 \right)^2 - 1 + \left\{ \left[1 - \left(2\zeta \frac{K_v}{\omega_n} - 1 \right)^2 \right]^2 + 4 \frac{K_v^4}{\omega_n^4} \right\}^{1/2} \right] \right\}^{1/2}$$
$$(2.43)$$

If we suppose $\omega_n \ll K_v$, equation (2.43) simplifies and we obtain

$$\omega_1 \approx \omega_n [2\zeta^2 + (4\zeta^4 + 1)^{1/2}]^{1/2} \quad (2.44)$$

If we use the same approximation as $\omega_n \ll K_v$, the phase corresponding to the cut-off angular frequency can be obtained from

$$\Phi = \arctan 2\zeta [2\zeta^2 + (4\zeta^4 + 1)^{1/2}]^{1/2} - 180° \quad (2.45)$$

and the phase margin is

$$\Phi_M = \arctan 2\zeta [2\zeta^2 + (4\zeta^4 + 1)^{1/2}]^{1/2} \quad (2.46)$$

If a phase margin of 45° is required equation (2.46) gives a lower limit of 0.42 for the damping factor.

From equations (2.40) and (2.41) we obtain the Bode diagram (Fig. 2.9).

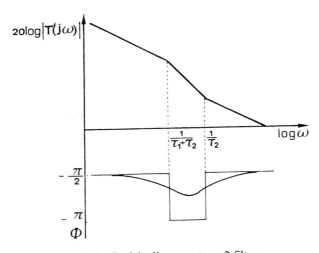

Fig. 2.9   Bode's diagram: type 2 filter.

(e)   Conclusions

The fact that the term $1 + s\tau_2$ is present in the loop studied so far gives a number of advantages. In particular, if a narrow band pass is required, and the resistance R_2 can be chosen so that the damping factor ensures device stability. The system is said to have been compensated with phase advance, if compared with the device using a filter of type 1.

2.4.3   Active low pass filter with a pole and a zero (type 3)

The schematic of the filter is given in Fig. 2.10. The transfer function of the filter is as follows:

$$F(s) = \frac{1 + s\tau_2}{\tau_1 s} \tag{2.47}$$

(a)   Closed-loop transfer function

Its expression is

$$T(s) = \frac{K_v F(s)}{s + K_v F(s)}$$

Substituting equation (2.47) into the previous equation gives

$$T(s) = \frac{K_v(s\tau_2 + 1)/\tau_1}{s^2 + (\tau_2/\tau_1)K_v s + K_v/\tau_1} \tag{2.48}$$

In order to normalize the previous equation, we introduce the following notations:

$$2\zeta\omega_n = \frac{\tau_2}{\tau_1} K_v$$

$$\tag{2.49}$$

$$\omega_n^2 = \frac{K_v}{\tau_1}$$

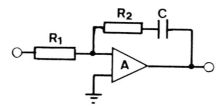

Fig. 2.10   Filter of type 3.

2. The root loci terminate on the zero $s = -1/\tau_2$ where $K_v = \infty$.
3. *Section of the root loci lying on the real axis.* To the right of the zero $-1/\tau_2$ there is a double pole, and therefore no point lies on the root loci. The segment between the pole $-1/\tau_3$ and the zero $-1/\tau_2$ lies on the loci because to the right of the pole there is a zero and a double pole. Finally, the portion of the real axis located to the left of the pole $-1/\tau_3$ does not belong to the loci since one zero and three poles are located to the right of the pole.
4. *Points of departure of root locus from real axis.* They depart as soon as the roots they represent become complex conjugates.
5. *Asymptotes.* For values of s tending towards infinity, we have

$$T'(s)_{s \Rightarrow \infty} \to K_v \frac{\tau_2}{\tau_1 \tau_3} s^{-2} \to 0$$

The angles that the asymptotes make with the real axis are given by

$$-(1 + 2k)\frac{\pi}{2}$$

that is to say $-90°$ and $90°$. Therefore, we have an asymptote perpendicular to the real axis.

The asymptotes meet at a point located along the real axis and determined by the following relationship

$$\sigma_a = \left(\sum s_j - \sum z_i\right)\frac{1}{n - m}$$
$$= \frac{-1/\tau_2 + 1/\tau_3}{2}$$

Following this result it is worth noting that the asymptote meets the real axis at infinity when $\tau_3 = 0$. In such a case the system is no more of the third degree but of the second degree.

The roots of equation (2.62) are either all three real or one real and two complex conjugate. We already have determined the real sections of the root loci; we still have to determine those related with the complex roots. Instead of studying the general case, we shall study a particular case in order to know the appearance of the loci. For this particular case, we set $\tau_1 = 1$ s and $\tau_2 = 0.2$ s into equation (2.62), and we obtain

$$\tau_3 s^3 + s^2 + 0.2\,K_v s + K_v^2 = 0$$

The loci are drawn by varying K_v and taking τ_3 as a parameter. Thus, to each value of the time constant corresponds some particular locus. Results are illustrated in Fig. 2.19.

Examination of the root loci shows the influence of the time constant τ_3. The lower its value is, the more we approximate to a second-order system. From a certain value the root locus crosses the real axis, giving rise to a closed curve with which is associated an asymptote perpendicular to the real axis, crossing it at a point located at a distance which increases when τ_3 decreases; at the same time the closed curve approaches a circle. On the contrary, if it increases, for a certain value, the closed curve vanishes and the asymptote shifts closer to the imaginary axis. The closer it comes, the less stable is the system. In the example given, it becomes unstable when $\tau_3 = \tau_2 = 0.2\,\text{s}$. In this case the asymptote coincides with the imaginary axis, which becomes the root locus. Of course, if τ_3 becomes greater than τ_2, the real part of the roots becomes positive and the system becomes unconditionally unstable. The stability criterion that we shall use, as we shall see later on, will be related to the angle that the semistraight line crossing the origin makes with the real axis. We shall come to that after the study of the stability by Bode's method.

(e)   Stability determined by Bode's method

Let us replace s with $j\omega$ in equation (2.60) and then calculate the magnitude of $|T'(j\omega)|$. We also need the phase Φ which has already been calculated and is given by equation (2.61).

From these two equations we can plot the Bode diagram, illustrated in Fig. 2.15. As far as the phase is concerned, the diagram reveals a maximum for a certain value of the angular frequency. If its magnitude were unity at such an angular frequency, we would obtain the maximum phase margin.

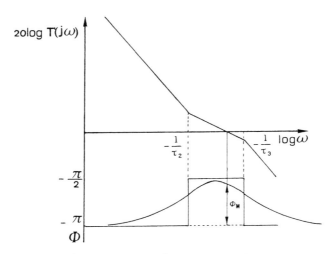

Fig. 2.15   Bode's diagram: type 4 filter.

2.5.2 Optimization of a third-order loop

(a) Definition of the damping factor and the natural angular frequency

Let us consider the s plane where are represented the roots of the characteristic equation (2.62):

$$s^3 + \frac{1}{\tau_3}s^2 + \frac{K_v \tau_2}{\tau_1 \tau_3}s + \frac{K_v}{\tau_1 \tau_3} = 0$$

The roots are

$$\begin{aligned} s_1 &= c & c &< 0 \\ s_2 &= a + jb & a &< 0 \\ s_3 &= a - jb & b &> 0 \end{aligned}$$

On the analogy of the second-order systems let us define a pseudo-damping factor and a pseudo-natural angular frequency:

$$\zeta = \cos \psi = \cos \left(\arctan \frac{b}{a} \right) = \frac{a}{(a^2 + b^2)^{1/2}}$$

$$a = -\omega_n \zeta \tag{2.63}$$

$$\omega_n^2 = a^2 + b^2$$

Figure 2.16 illustrates the preceding definitions in the s plane.
  Equation (2.62) can be written

$$(s - c)[s - (a + jb)][s - (a - jb)] = 0$$

After expanding this, we find

$$s^3 - (2a + c)s^2 + (a^2 + b^2 + 2ac)s - c(a^2 + b^2) = 0$$

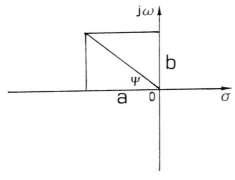

Fig. 2.16 Pseudo-damping factor and pseudo-natural angular frequency.

Making use of relations (2.63), in the above equation, we obtain

$$s^3 + (2\zeta\omega_n - c)s^2 + (\omega_n^2 - 2\zeta\omega_n c)s - c\omega_n^2 = 0 \qquad (2.64)$$

Identification of the polynomial coefficients with those of equation (2.62) leads to

$$2\zeta\omega_n - c = \frac{1}{\tau_3}$$

$$\omega_n^2 - 2\zeta\omega_n c = K_v \frac{\tau_2}{\tau_1 \tau_3} = -c\omega_n^2 \tau_2 \qquad (2.65)$$

$$-c\omega_n^2 = \frac{K_v}{\tau_1 \tau_3}$$

(b)   Particular conditions leading to simple calculations

In order to simplify the solution of equation (2.64), which is of the third order, we shall consider a particular case related to the phase margin. We have observed, in the Bode diagram, that the phase Φ presents a maximum and that in order to optimize the phase margin the magnitude of $|T'(j\omega)|$ should equal unity.

Rather than determine the angular frequency for which the phase is at a maximum, using equation (2.61) we shall calculate it from the expression of the phase margin.

Let us from equation (2.61) deduce the phase margin

$$\Phi_M = \arctan \omega\tau_2 - \arctan \omega\tau_3 \qquad (2.66)$$

Let us find the angular frequency ω_M for which the derivative of Φ_M is zero; we obtain

$$\frac{d\Phi_M}{d\omega} = \frac{\tau_2}{1 + \omega_M^2\tau_2^2} - \frac{\tau_3}{1 + \omega_M^2\tau_3^2} = 0$$

and then

$$\tau_2 + \omega_M^2\tau_3^2\tau_2 - \tau_3 - \omega_M^2\tau_2^2\tau_3 = 0$$

from which we deduce

$$\omega_M^2 = \frac{1}{\tau_2\tau_3} \qquad (2.67)$$

Equation (2.66) allows the calculation of $\tan \Phi_M$; we obtain

$$\tan \Phi_M = \frac{\omega\tau_2 - \omega\tau_3}{1 + \omega^2\tau_2\tau_3} \qquad (2.68)$$

From equations (2.67) and (2.68) we obtain

$$2 \tan \Phi_M = \frac{\tau_2 - \tau_3}{(\tau_2 \tau_3)^{1/2}}$$

$$= \frac{1}{\omega_M \tau_3} - \omega_M \tau_3$$

and, if we take into account the last relationship,

$$\omega_M^2 \tau_3^2 + 2\omega_M \tan \Phi_M \tau_3 - 1 = 0$$

The only acceptable solution regarding τ_3 is

$$\tau_3 = -\frac{\tan \Phi_M}{\omega_M} + \frac{1}{\omega_M^2}(\omega_M^2 \tan^2 \Phi_M + \omega_M^2)^{1/2}$$

$$= \frac{1}{\omega_M}\left(-\tan \Phi_M + \frac{1}{\cos \Phi_M}\right) \qquad (2.69)$$

$$= \frac{1}{\omega_M} \frac{1 - \sin \Phi_M}{\cos \Phi_M}$$

Notice that, for $\Phi_M = \pi/2$, we obtain the indeterminate expression $0/0$, whose limit can be obtained using L'Hospital's rule; we find

$$\frac{\cos \Phi_M}{\sin \Phi_M}$$

whose limiting value is 0.

We see that it is not possible, with such a system, to have a phase margin larger than 90° because if $\tau_3 = 0$ the device is of the second order.

In equation (2.67) ω_M is equal to $1/(\tau_2 \tau_3)^{1/2}$. Therefore, since τ_2 and τ_3 are functions of ζ, ω_n and c, we shall obtain an equation of the following form:

$$f(\zeta, \omega_n, c, \Phi_M) = 0$$

If we make use of the normal parameters, that is to say ζ and ω_n plus the constraint imposed by the margin phase Φ_M, it will be possible to calculate c, the real root, from a second-degree equation. Once a root of the characteristic equation is known, the calculation of the other two roots is trivial.

From equations (2.65) we obtain

$$\tau_3 = \frac{1}{2\zeta\omega_n - c}$$

$$\tau_2 = -\frac{\omega_n - 2\zeta c}{c\omega_n}$$

Thus

$$\frac{1}{\omega_M} = \left[\frac{\omega_n - 2\zeta c}{-c\omega_n(2\zeta\omega_n - c)} \right]^{1/2} \tag{2.70}$$

and

$$\frac{1}{2\zeta\omega_n - c} = \left[\frac{\omega_n - 2\zeta c}{-c\omega_n(2\zeta\omega_n - c)} \right]^{1/2} \frac{1 - \sin \Phi_M}{\cos \Phi_M}$$

Squaring both sides of this last expression, we find the equation we were looking for, i.e.

$$c^2 - c\frac{\omega_n}{2\zeta}\left[1 + 4\zeta^2 - \left(\frac{\cos \Phi_M}{1 - \sin \Phi_M} \right)^2 \right] + \omega_n^2 = 0 \tag{2.71}$$

whose roots are

$$c = \frac{\omega_n}{4\zeta}\left[1 + 4\zeta^2 - \left(\frac{\cos \Phi_M}{1 - \sin \Phi_M} \right)^2 \pm \left\{ \left[1 + 4\zeta^2 - \left(\frac{\cos \Phi_M}{1 - \sin \Phi_M} \right)^2 \right]^2 - 16\zeta^2 \right\}^{1/2} \right] \tag{2.71'}$$

The Bode diagram shows (Fig. 2.15) that only one value of the gain K_v for which the phase is at a maximum exists. Therefore, equation (2.71) has only one solution and its discriminant must be null, and then the following condition is required:

$$\left(\frac{\cos \Phi_M}{1 - \sin \Phi_M} \right)^2 = 4\zeta^2 \pm 4\zeta + 1 = (1 \pm 2\zeta)^2 \tag{2.72}$$

Only the solution

$$\frac{\cos \Phi_M}{1 - \sin \Phi_M} = 1 + 2\zeta \tag{2.73}$$

is compatible with the physical constraints. By simple trigonometric algebra, it can be written as follows:

$$\tan \Phi_M = \frac{2\zeta(\zeta + 1)}{1 + 2\zeta} \tag{2.74}$$

The real root is then equal to $-\omega_n$, and thus if we replace c with this value in equation (2.70) we find $\omega_M = \omega_n$.

The same result can be found from the following condition:

$$|T'(j\omega_M)| = 1 \tag{2.75}$$

From equation (2.60), we have

$$|T'(j\omega)| = \frac{K_v}{\tau_1\omega^2}\left(\frac{1 + \tau_2^2\omega^2}{1 + \tau_3^2\omega^2} \right)^{1/2} \tag{2.76}$$

and thus

$$\frac{K_v}{\tau_1 \omega_M^2} \left(\frac{1 + \tau_2^2 \omega_M^2}{1 + \tau_3^2 \omega_M^2} \right)^{1/2} = 1 \qquad (2.77)$$

Let us replace ω_M with its value obtained from equation (2.67) and then let us calculate K_v; we find

$$K_v = \frac{\tau_1}{\tau_2} \left(\frac{1}{\tau_2 \tau_3} \right)^{1/2} \qquad (2.78)$$

In the Bode diagram, this expression indicates the value that the gain K_v has to have so that the magnitude of $|T'(j\omega_M)|$ should cross the straight line $0\,\mathrm{dB}$ at a point where the phase is at a maximum.

The preceding condition is optimum but nevertheless it does not ensure that the phase margin is larger than $45°$.

Let us look for a relationship between ω_n and ω_M.

The time constants τ_i are functions of ζ, ω_n and c that we can calculate from equations (2.65). We find

$$\tau_3 = \frac{1}{2\zeta \omega_n - c}$$

$$\tau_2 = \frac{\omega_n - 2\zeta c}{-c\omega_n}$$

$$\tau_1 = -\frac{K_v}{c\omega_n^2}(2\zeta\omega_n - c) \qquad (2.79)$$

$$\frac{\tau_2}{\tau_1} = \frac{\omega_n(\omega_n - 2\zeta c)}{K_v(2\zeta\omega_n - c)}$$

Next, eliminating K_v between equations (2.78) and the last of equations (2.79) and with the help of equation (2.67), we find the relationship we were looking for, that is to say

$$\omega_M = \omega_n \frac{\omega_n - 2\zeta c}{2\zeta\omega_n - c} \qquad (2.80)$$

and if $\omega_M = \omega_n$, we obtain

$$-c = \omega_n = \omega_M$$

This result shows that there is only one solution for c.

A very important result will be established now. Let us consider the gain K_v along the root loci. With each of its values is associated at least one real root. Therefore, when a semistraight line starting from the origin cuts the locus in two points, to each of these points corresponds a real root: c_1 and c_2. If the discriminant of equation (2.71') is null there is only one value for the real root

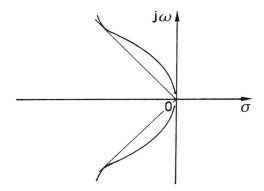

Fig. 2.17   Semistraight lines tangential to the root loci.

c and the semistraight lines starting from the origin are tangential to the corresponding branch of the root loci (Fig. 2.17).

If this is the case, we deduce

1. the existence of only one real root *c* equal to $-\omega_n$,
2. a cut-off angular frequency ω_1 equal to ω_n, and
3. a phase margin Φ_M equal to its maximum value.

Let us determine the damping factor corresponding to a phase margin of 45°; it is obtained from equation (2.74). The result is $\zeta = \sqrt{2}/2$.

In the same way let us calculate the phase margin corresponding to $\zeta = 1$. The previous formula gives $\Phi_M = 53.13$.

The time constant formulas become

$$\tau_3 = \frac{1}{\omega_n(1 + 2\zeta)} \tag{2.81}$$

$$\tau_2 = \frac{1 + 2\zeta}{\omega_n} \tag{2.82}$$

$$\tau_1 = \frac{K_v}{\omega_n^2}(1 + 2\zeta) \tag{2.83}$$

$$\frac{\tau_2}{\tau_1} = \frac{\omega_n}{K_v} \tag{2.84}$$

$$\frac{\tau_3}{\tau_2} = \frac{1}{(1 + 2\zeta)^2} \tag{2.85}$$

The characteristic equation is written as follows:

$$(s + \omega_n)(s^2 + 2\zeta\omega_n s + \omega_n^2) = 0 \tag{2.86a}$$

$$s^3 + \omega_n(1 + 2\zeta)s^2 + \omega_n^2(1 + 2\zeta)s + \omega_n^3 = 0 \tag{2.86b}$$

The real root as well as the real and imaginary parts of the complex conjugate roots are

$$c = -\omega_n$$
$$a = -\zeta\omega_n$$
$$b = (1 - \zeta^2)^{1/2}\omega_n$$

Therefore, it is not necessary to use a third-degree equation to calculate them.

(c)   Locus of the tangent points

Let us recall that we are dealing with the points where the semistraight lines starting from the origin are tangential to the root loci.

Let Ψ be the angle as defined in Fig. 2.18. In order that the above-defined semistraight lines should be tangential to the root loci, the damping factor $\zeta = \cos \Psi$ must fulfil the conditions expressed by equations (2.67) and (2.85).

From equation (2.85), we obtain

$$\zeta = \cos \Psi = \frac{(\tau_2/\tau_3)^{1/2} - 1}{2}$$

Next, eliminating τ_3 between the last equation and equation (2.67), we find the following result:

$$\frac{1}{\tau_2^2} = \frac{\omega_M^2}{(2 \cos \Psi + 1)^2} \tag{2.86c}$$

Setting $1/\tau_2 = R$, equation (2.86b) becomes

$$\omega_M^2 = R^2(2 \cos \Psi + 1)^2$$

but

$$\omega_M = \omega_n = (a^2 + b^2)^{1/2}$$

Therefore, if M belongs to the locus, then we have

$$OM = \rho = \pm R(2 \cos \Psi + 1) \tag{2.87}$$

which is the equation, in polar coordinates, of a Pascal's snail.

This locus can be obtained in the following way. First draw the circle of radius $R = 1/\tau_2$ whose centre is at $(-1/\tau_2, 0)$. Let N be a point of the circle. The radius vector $OM = \rho$ is obtained by adding $NM = R$ to $ON = 2R \cos \psi$. The point N moves along the circle whose radius is R and the point M belonging to the Pascal's snail is obtained lengthening ON of the amount R.

Figure 2.18 illustrates Pascal's snail and its construction. Pascal's snail is very interesting for drawing an accurate root locus, as will be seen in the next section.

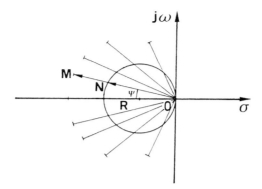

Fig. 2.18   Pascal's snail.

(d)   Accurate drawing of the root loci

The root locus tangential to the real axis is of great interest. The point where curves are tangential corresponds to a triple root equal to $3R = \omega_n$. In the particular case shown at the end of section 2.5.1(d), this root is equal to $-15\,\text{s}^{-1}$.

From equations (2.81) and (2.83) we calculate $1/\tau_3$ and K_v; we obtain

$$\frac{1}{\tau_3} = 45\,\text{s}^{-1}$$

$$K_v = 75\,\text{s}^{-1}$$

and the characteristic equation becomes

$$\frac{1}{45}s^3 + s^2 + 15\,s + 75 = 0 \tag{2.88}$$

We can verify that this equation has a triple root equal to $-15\,\text{s}^{-1}$.

As indicated in section 2.5.1(d) the root locus was drawn by varying K_v and taking τ_3 as a parameter. Thus, to each value of τ_3 corresponds a particular root locus (Fig. 2.19).

Let us recall that the root loci correspond to the particular case where $\tau_1 = 1\,\text{s}$ and $\tau_2 = 0.2\,\text{s}$. The equation of Pascal's snail is then

$$\rho = 5(2\cos\Psi + 1)$$

Its plot allows us to determine the points where the root locus is tangential to the semistraight lines from the origin along which the damping factor is constant.

Using different values Ψ, between 0 and $\pi/2$, we calculate the corresponding values of τ_3. With each of these values we associate an equation of the third degree, and we calculate its roots. As we have already mentioned, a very important curve is the one which is tangential to the real axis. The angle Ψ is then equal

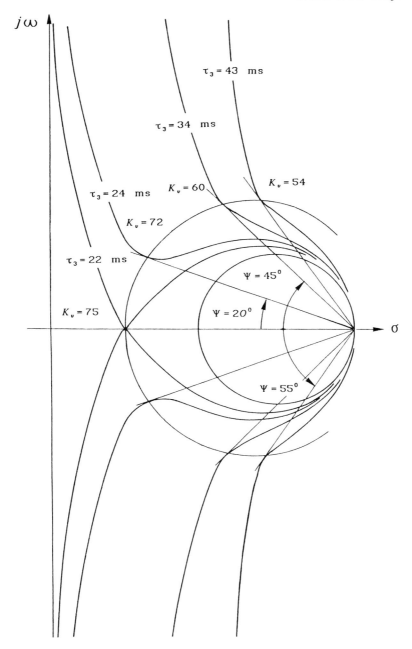

Fig. 2.19 Root loci: type 4 filter.

to 0; we then have

$$\tau_3 = \frac{\tau_2}{(2\cos\Psi + 1)^2} = \frac{0.2}{(2+1)^2}\,s = 0.0222\,s$$

Moreover, the root is a triple one whose value is

$$-c = \omega_n = \frac{1}{(\tau_2\tau_3)^{1/2}} = \frac{1}{(0.2 \times 0.0222)^{1/2}}\,s^{-1} = 15\,s^{-1}$$

This result confirms the value already calculated from equation (2.88).

In the same manner, we can determine the curve tangential to the semistraight line whose damping factor is $\sqrt{2}/2$. A similar calculation to the previous one gives

$$\tau_3 = 0.0343\,s; \quad c = -12.07\,s^{-1}$$

The asymptotes intercept the real axis at

$$\sigma = \frac{-1/\tau_2 + 1/\tau_3}{2} = \frac{-5 + 1/\tau_3}{2}$$

Thus, we find

$$-19.5\,s^{-1}, 12.08\,s^{-1}$$

In the example studied so far, the previous results are no longer valid when $\tau_3 < 0.0222\,s$. As a matter of fact, from the above value, the locus gives rise to two branches and one of them is a closed curve. The last approaches more and more a circle whose radius is $1/\tau_2$ and which is the root locus of a second-order system and therefore $\tau_3 = 0$. As a first approximation, we can consider the system equivalent to a second-order one, as soon as we have reached the value of τ_3 that splits the locus into two.

(e)   Normalized root loci

Let us write equation (2.62) putting $K_v/\tau_1 = K$ and $1/\tau_3 = \lambda$; we obtain

$$\frac{1}{\lambda}s^3 + s^2 + K\tau_2 s + K = 0 \tag{2.89}$$

Let us take τ_2 as a unit of time, expressed in seconds. Thus, we have the following new variables:

$$\sigma' = \tau_2\sigma$$
$$\omega' = \tau_2\omega$$
$$K' = \tau_2^2 K$$
$$\lambda' = \frac{\tau_2}{\tau_3}$$
$$s' = \tau_2\sigma + j\tau_2\frac{2\pi}{T}$$

Equations (2.81), (2.82) and (2.84), using these new variables, become

$$\tau'_3 = \frac{1}{(1 + 2\zeta)^2} = \frac{1}{\lambda'}$$

$$\omega'_n = 1 + 2\zeta$$

$$K' = \omega'_n = 1 + 2\zeta = \lambda'^{1/2}$$

and equation (2.89) is now re-written as

$$\frac{1}{\lambda'}s'^3 + s'^2 + K's' + K' = 0 \tag{2.90}$$

Eventually, it takes the following form:

$$\frac{1}{\lambda'}s'^3 + s'^2 + \lambda'^{1/2}s' + \lambda'^{1/2} = 0 \tag{2.91}$$

The normalized root locus is obtained with a gain equal to K' and

$$\lambda' = \frac{1}{\tau'_3} = (1 + 2\cos \Psi)^2$$

as a parameter.

We first draw the Pascal's snail from a circle whose radius is unity, adding to the vector radius the unit length. Each point that is tangential to the semistraight lines from the origin is marked with the gain value, calculated from

$$K' = 1 + 2\zeta = 1 + 2\cos \Psi$$

$$= \lambda'^{1/2}$$

and on each root locus we mark the value of the corresponding parameter λ'.

The normalized root loci are thus obtained and are illustrated in Fig. 2.20. As we can see, they are the same as those corresponding to the particular case studied in section 2.5.1(d) (Fig. 2.19): only the marked values are different.

Important remark. In order to simplify a project where a third-order loop is required it is worthwhile using the simple formulas corresponding to the tangent point. As far as the damping factor is concerned its limits are between 0.7 and 1. Moreover, the phase margin is linked to that choice. Let us recall that if 0.7 is chosen the phase margin is then 45°.

The following examples will show the reader the simplicity of such an approach although a third-order loop is used.

2.5.3 Specific examples

Let us use a few results, some of them to be established in Chapter 9, which will permit us to illustrate some examples in which third-order loops are involved.

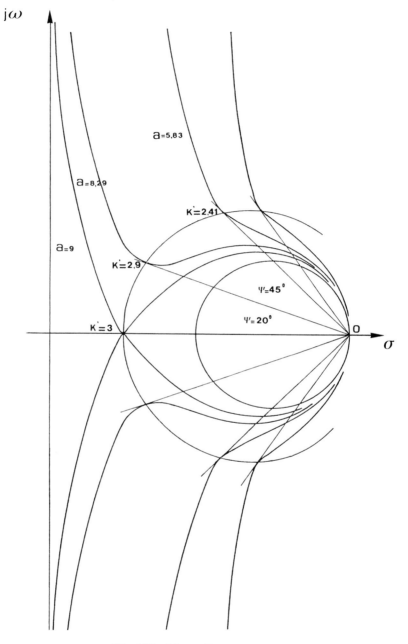

Fig. 2.20   Normalized root loci.

(a) Example 1

The characteristic equation of the transfer function of a motor speed control with PLL is as follows:

$$s^3 + \frac{1}{T_m}s^2 + \frac{K}{T_m}s + \frac{K}{T_m \tau_2} = 0 \qquad (2.92)$$

where K (expressed in reciprocal seconds) is a constant of the loop, τ_2 is a time constant equal to $R_2 C$ of a type 2 filter and T_m is the motor time constant.

What is the value of τ_2 required in order that the system should be stable?

To ensure good stability we choose the following values:

$$\zeta = \frac{\sqrt{2}}{2}$$

$$\Phi_M = 45°$$

This choice allows us to use the characteristic equation obtained from equation (2.86b):

$$s^3 + 2.41\,\omega_n s^2 + 2.41\,\omega_n^2 s + \omega_n^3 = 0$$

Identifying the terms of the previous equations, we find

$$\frac{1}{T_m} = 2.41\,\omega_n$$

$$\frac{K}{T_m} = 2.41\,\omega_n^2$$

$$\frac{K}{T_m \tau_2} = \omega_n^3$$

Since $T_m = 0.05\,\text{s}$, from the first equation we calculate

$$\omega_n = \frac{1}{2.41\,T_m} = 8.3\,\text{rad s}^{-1}$$

and we find using the two other equations

$$\frac{K}{T_m} = (8.3)^2 \times 2.41 \approx 166$$

$$\frac{K}{T_m \tau_2} = \frac{2.41\,\omega_n^2}{0.29} \approx 572$$

$$\tau_2 \approx 0.29\,\text{s}$$

$$K = 166 \times 0.05 = 8.3$$

Taking into account the values just calculated, the characteristic equation takes the following form:

$$s^3 + 20s^2 + 166s + 572 = 0$$

As a check the complex conjugate roots are calculated:

$$c = \omega_n = -8.3$$
$$a = -\zeta\omega_n = -5.85$$
$$b = (1 - \zeta^2)^{1/2}\omega_n = 5.89$$

Then, we proceed with the calculation of all the characteristics and we find

$$\zeta = \cos\left(\arctan\frac{b}{a}\right) = 0.7$$

$$\omega_n = (a^2 + b^2)^{1/2} = 8.3$$
$$\Phi_M = \arctan\omega_n\tau_2 - \arctan\omega_n T_m$$
$$\Phi_M = \arctan 8.3 \times 0.29 - \arctan 8.3 \times 0.05$$
$$\Phi_M = 66.44° - 22.54° = 44.9°$$

$$|T(j\omega_n)| = K\frac{\tau_2}{\tau_2}\frac{1}{\omega_n^2}\left[\frac{(1/\tau_2)^2 + \omega_2^2}{(1/T_m)^2 + \omega_n^2}\right]^{1/2}$$

$$= \frac{166}{(8.3)^2}\left[\frac{11.89 + (8.3)^2}{400 + (8.3)^2}\right]^{1/2} = 1$$

(b) Example 2

A PLL device oscillates at 5000 Hz and its natural frequency is 500 Hz. We have $K_d = 2\,\text{V rad}^{-1}$ and $K_0 = 2\pi \times 5000\,\text{rad s}^{-1}\,\text{V}^{-1}$. We are bound by the following constraints

$$\zeta = \frac{\sqrt{2}}{2}$$

$$\Phi_M = 45°$$

Determine the time constants τ_3, τ_2 and τ_1.
 We have

$$\tau_3 = \frac{1}{(1 + 2\zeta)\omega_n}$$

$$= \frac{1}{2.41 \times 500 \times 2 \times \pi}\,\text{s}$$

$$= 1.32 \times 10^{-4}\,\text{s}$$

and

$$\tau_2 = \lambda' \tau_3$$
$$= 5.83 \times 1.32 \times 10^{-10}\,\text{s}$$
$$= 7.7 \times 10^{-4}\,\text{s}$$

K is then calculated

$$K = \frac{\lambda'^{1/2}}{\tau_2^2}$$
$$= 5\frac{(83)^{1/2}}{(7.7 \times 10^{-4})^2}$$
$$= 4.07 \times 10^6$$

and therefore

$$\tau_1 = \frac{K_d K_0}{K}$$
$$= \frac{2\pi \times 5000 \times 2}{4.08 \times 10^6}\,\text{s}$$
$$= 1.54 \times 10^{-2}\,\text{s}$$

3

Linear tracking

In Chapter 2 we saw the open- and closed-loop transfer functions from which we studied the stability using the Evans and Bode methods. A type of third-order loop which is used in many applications was characterized and a method was developed allowing simplification of the calculations with which the designer is normally confronted.

In this third chapter we shall see how the device tracks the input signal. Therefore, its output will be compared with its input in order to determine the tracking performance of the system. The tracking tests will be carried out using several excitation functions applied to the input.

3.1 DEFINITIONS

3.1.1 Accuracy

As we saw in Chapter 2, Fig. 2.2 (repeated here as Fig. 3.1) illustrates the block diagram of a PLL system in the complex frequency domain.

Accuracy is defined as follows:

$$\Theta_e(s) = \Theta_r(s) - \Theta_1(s) \tag{3.1}$$

and according to Fig. 3.1

$$\Theta_1(s) = \Theta_e(s) K_d F(s) \frac{K_0}{s}$$

$$\Theta_1(s) = \Theta_e(s) K_v \frac{F(s)}{s}$$

Replacing the above expression in equation (3.1), we obtain

$$\Theta_e(s) = \Theta_r(s) - \Theta_r(s) K_v \frac{F(s)}{s}$$

from which we obtain, taking into account equation (2.17),

$$\Theta_e(s) = \frac{s \, \Theta_r(s)}{s + K_v F(s)} = [1 - T(s)] \Theta_r(s) \tag{3.2}$$

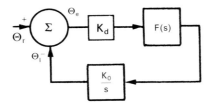

Fig. 3.1 PLL block diagram.

3.1.2 Steady-state error

We define the static accuracy as the value taken by $\theta_e(t)$ in the steady-state condition, that is to say $\theta_e(\infty)$.

We define an nth-order stationary error as the limit taken by $\theta_e(\infty)$ when $t \to \infty$ and which corresponds to an input $\theta_{1n}(t)$ such that

$$\theta_{1n}(t) = \frac{t^{n-1}}{(n-1)!} u_1(t) \tag{3.3}$$

whose Laplace transform is

$$\Theta_{1n}(s) = \frac{1}{s^n} \tag{3.4}$$

We shall limit ourselves to first-, second- and third-order steady-state errors. They are related to the following input signals:

$$\theta_{11}(t) = u_1(t)$$

$$\theta_{12}(t) = t u_1(t)$$

$$\theta_{13}(t) = \frac{t^2}{2} u_1(t)$$

The resulting errors are termed position, velocity and acceleration, or dynamic tracking.

The Laplace transforms of the signals $\theta_{1n}(t)$ are

$$\Theta_{11}(s) = \frac{1}{s}$$

$$\Theta_{12}(s) = \frac{1}{s^2}$$

$$\Theta_{13}(s) = \frac{1}{s^3}$$

3.1.3   Transient error

The transient error corresponds to the transient response of a system if its value is not negligible. It is characterized by the function $\theta_e(t)$ when the input of the loop is driven by a signal of the form $\theta_{1n}(t)$.

3.2   APPLICATION TO THE PLL

3.2.1   Excitation input signals

The phase step is

$$\Delta\theta_{11}(t) = \Delta\phi u_1(t)$$

the angular frequency step is

$$\Delta\theta_{12}(t) = \Delta\omega t u_1(t)$$

and the acceleration step is

$$\Delta\theta_{13}(t) = \tfrac{1}{2}\Delta\dot\omega t^2 u_1(t)$$

where

$$\Delta\dot\omega = \frac{d\omega}{dt} = \frac{d^2\theta}{dt^2} \ (\text{rad s}^{-2})$$

$\Delta\dot\omega$ being the rate of change of the angular frequency. If it is constant, we obtain

$$\frac{d\theta(t)}{dt} = \Delta\dot\omega t$$

$$\theta(t) = \tfrac{1}{2}\Delta\dot\omega t^2$$

then, putting $\theta(t) = \Delta\theta_{13}/u_1(t)$, we find

$$\Delta\theta_{13}(t) = \tfrac{1}{2}\Delta\dot\omega t^2 u_1(t)$$

The Laplace transforms of the preceding signals are

$$\Delta\Theta_{11}(s) = \frac{\Delta\phi}{s}$$

$$\Delta\Theta_{12}(s) = \frac{\Delta\omega}{s^2}$$

$$\Delta\Theta_{13}(s) = \frac{\Delta\dot\omega}{s^3}$$

3.2.2   Steady-state error

In order to calculate the steady-state error, the final value theorem is applied. That is to say,

$$[\theta_e(t)]_{t\to\infty} = \lim_{s\to 0} s\frac{s\,\Theta_r(s)}{s + K_v F(s)}$$

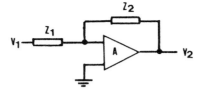

Fig. 3.2 Operational amplifier.

Note. The transfer function expressions in Fig. 2.3 show that $F(s) \to 1$ when s approaches 0 for the two passive filters, and ∞ for the active ones.

This result is due to the fact that an approximate formula, regarding the voltage gain, is used for the active filters

$$G = -\frac{Z_2}{Z_1}$$

A more accurate formula for the gain is (Fig. 3.2)

$$G = \frac{v_2}{v_1} = -\frac{1}{1/A + (Z_1/Z_2)(1 + 1/A)}$$

which shows that $v_2/v_1 \to -A$ when $Z_2 \to \infty$, Z_1 being equal to R_1. Therefore, $|F(0)| = A$.

(a)   Phase error due to a phase step

We have to calculate

$$[\theta_{e1}(t)]_{t \to \infty} = \lim_{s \to 0} \frac{s\Delta\phi}{s + K_v F(s)}$$

for each filter. The calculation is trivial and we obtain a null error for each filter.

(b)   Phase error due to an angular frequency step

We have

$$[\theta_{e2}(t)]_{t \to \infty} = \lim_{s \to 0} \frac{\Delta\omega}{s + K_v F(s)} = \frac{\Delta\omega}{K_v F(0)}$$

and we find respectively for each filter, passive and active,

$$\frac{\Delta\omega}{K_v}, \quad \frac{\Delta\omega}{A K_v}$$

Therefore, the active filters allow us to reduce the velocity error drastically since it is divided by the gain of the operational amplifier.

(c)   Angular frequency error due to an angular frequency step

The relationship

$$\Theta(s) = \frac{\Omega(s)}{s}$$

allows the angular frequency error calculation; we obtain

$$\Omega_e(s) = \frac{s\,\Omega_r(s)}{s + K_v F(s)}$$

When an angular frequency step is applied, whose Laplace transform is $\Delta\omega/s$, the final value theorem shows that the angular frequency error is zero for any filter. This means that both the frequency of the reference signal and the frequency of oscillator are equal.

(d)   Angular frequency error due to an angular frequency ramp signal

Let $\omega_r = \Delta\dot\omega t$ be the frequency ramp whose Laplace transform is

$$\Omega_r(s) = \frac{\Delta\dot\omega}{s^2}$$

An identical calculation to that of section 3.2.2 (b) gives the frequency error in the case of a passive filter and in the case of an active filter, respectively:

$$\frac{\Delta\dot\omega}{K_v}, \quad \frac{\Delta\dot\omega}{AK_v}$$

Thus, when an angular frequency ramp signal is applied, the oscillator follows the reference with a certain lag. It is practically null when active filters are used.

(e)   Phase error due to an angular frequency ramp signal

If the final value theorem were applied, using the input signal

$$\Delta\Theta(s) = \frac{\Delta\dot\omega}{s^3}$$

we would find

$$[\theta_{e3}(t)]_{t\to\infty} = \lim_{s\to0} \frac{\Delta\dot\omega}{s[s + K_v F(s)]}$$

If this formula is applied to the passive or active filters we have studied so far, we find an infinite value. In reality, this formula cannot be applied since θ_{e3} is not small. Neither can it be applied with $\sin\theta_{e3}$. In fact, what happens is that, when the phase error reaches $\pi/2$, the system unlocks. Therefore, it is no longer linear and the theory does not hold any more.

Regarding the active filters, type 3 or 4, we find a finite value if we use the transfer functions $F(s)$ from equations (2.47) or (2.58) (we have seen that they are not valid when s approaches 0). Substituting them into the error expression and letting $s \to 0$, we obtain

$$[\theta_{e3}(t)]_{t \to \infty} = \frac{\tau_1 \Delta\dot{\omega}}{K_v}$$

In the case of a type 3 filter, since $K_v/\tau_1 = \omega_n^2$, we have

$$\theta_{e3}(\infty) = \frac{\Delta\dot{\omega}}{\omega_n^2}$$

Best [2] and Gardner [3] found this result because they consider that their integrator is perfect. Therefore, the loop gain $K_d K_0 F(0)$ is infinite. In fact, its value is $K_d K_0 |A|$.

This problem can be studied in a different way using the results related to the angular frequency error due to an angular frequency ramp signal. It is worth recalling them:

$$\frac{\Delta\dot{\omega}}{K_v}, \quad \frac{\Delta\dot{\omega}}{AK_v}$$

Terming ω_e the angular frequency error and putting the natural frequency in the previous results, we find for the type 1, 2 and 3 filters

$$\omega_e = \frac{\Delta\dot{\omega}}{\tau\omega_n^2}$$

$$\omega_e = \frac{\Delta\dot{\omega}}{(\tau_1 + \tau_2)\omega_n^2}$$

$$\omega_e = \frac{\Delta\dot{\omega}}{\tau_1 A\omega_n^2}$$

Let t_n be the time at the end of which the phase reaches $\pi/2$. For the three filters, we obtain

$$t_1 = \frac{\pi}{2} \frac{\tau\omega_n^2}{\Delta\dot{\omega}}$$

$$t_2 = \frac{\pi}{2} \frac{(\tau_1 + \tau_2)\omega_n^2}{\Delta\dot{\omega}}$$

$$t_3 = \frac{\pi}{2} \frac{\tau_1 A\omega_n^2}{\Delta\dot{\omega}}$$

According to refs 2–4 the ratio $\Delta\dot{\omega}/\omega_n^2$ is close to $1/2$, and thus

$$t_1 = \tau\pi$$

$$t_2 = (\tau_1 + \tau_2)\pi$$

$$t_2 = \tau_1 A\pi$$

Results obtained so far are very approximate, but they give us an idea of what happens, depending on the filter that we are using. For instance, with a type 1 filter, the unlock will be quite rapid and a little bit less than with a type 2 filter. Owing to the gain of the amplifier of the type 3 filter, the time for the error to reach $\pi/2$ is markedly longer. Before this limit is reached, the oscillator will be outside its operation range.

3.2.3 Transient error

(a) Type 1 filter

A schematic of this filter is given in Fig. 2.1. Replacing in equation (3.2) $F(s)$ by $1/(1 + s\tau)$, we obtain

$$\Theta_e(s) = \frac{\Theta_r(s)s(s + 1/\tau)}{s^2 + s/\tau + K_v/\tau} \tag{3.5}$$

Phase step applied to the reference input. Let $\Delta\phi\, u_1(t)$ be a phase step whose Laplace transform is $\Delta\phi/s$. The corresponding phase error is given by the expression

$$\Theta_e(s) = \frac{\Delta\phi\,(s + 1/\tau)}{s^2 + s/\tau + K_v/\tau} \tag{3.6}$$

and we obtain for $t = 0$

$$\theta_e(0) = \lim_{s \to \infty} s\,\Delta\phi\,\frac{s + 1/\tau}{s^2 + s/\tau + K_v/\tau} = \Delta\phi$$

FIRST CASE
The characteristic equation, the denominator of expression (3.6), has two complex roots.

Equation (3.6) modifies to

$$\Theta_e(s) = \frac{s + k}{(s + \alpha)(s + \beta)}\,\Delta\phi$$

whose inverse Laplace transform is (from the table in section A.1.2 (g))

$$\theta_e(t) = \frac{(k - \alpha)e^{-\alpha t} - (k - \beta)e^{-\beta t}}{\beta - \alpha}\,\Delta\phi \tag{3.7}$$

The roots are

$$s_1 = -\alpha = a + jb$$
$$s_2 = -\beta = a - jb \tag{3.8}$$

from which we obtain

$$\beta - \alpha = 2jb$$
$$k - \alpha = k + a + jb$$
$$k - \beta = k + a - jb$$

Putting $k + a = B$ and replacing the previous values in equation (3.7), we find

$$\theta_e(t) = \frac{(B + jb)e^{(a + jb)t} - (B - jb)e^{(a - jb)t}}{2jb} \Delta\phi$$

This can be re-written as follows:

$$\theta_e(t) = \frac{e^{at}}{b} \frac{B(e^{jbt} - e^{-jbt}) + jb(e^{jbt} - e^{-jbt})}{2j} \Delta\phi$$

or, using Euler's relationships

$$\cos x = \frac{e^{jx} + e^{-jx}}{2}$$

$$\sin x = \frac{e^{jx} - e^{-jx}}{2j}$$

and finally

$$\theta_e(t) = \frac{\Delta\phi}{b} e^{at} (B \sin bt + b \cos bt) \tag{3.9}$$

SECOND CASE
The characteristic equation has a double root. Expression (3.6) can be re-written in the following form:

$$\Theta_e(s) = \Delta\phi \frac{s + k}{(s + \alpha)^2}$$

Therefore, from the Laplace transform pairs of the table in section A.1.2 (g), we deduce that the response function is

$$\theta_e(t) = \Delta\phi [(k - \alpha)t + 1]e^{-at}$$

Using relations (3.8) and setting b equal to 0, we find

$$\theta_e(t) = \Delta\phi [(k + a)t + 1]e^{at} \tag{3.10}$$

THIRD CASE

The denominator of equation (3.6) has two real roots:

$$p_1 = -\alpha = a + b'$$

$$p_2 = -\beta = a - b'$$

It is possible to obtain the results related to real roots from the results related to complex roots just by changing jb into b'. Following the calculations from which we obtained equation (3.9), we see that sin and cos become, respectively, sinh and cosh. Moreover, every time we meet terms such as

$$a^2 + b^2$$

they must be replaced by

$$a^2 - b'^2$$

Therefore, it is possible to deduce the result from the response related to complex roots. Then we obtain

$$\theta_e(t) = \frac{\Delta\phi}{b'} e^{at} (B \sinh b't + b' \cosh b't) \tag{3.11}$$

NORMALIZED EXPRESSIONS

If we put

$$k = \frac{1}{\tau} = 2\zeta\omega_n$$

$$\frac{K_v}{\tau} = \omega_n^2$$

then equation (3.6) is re-written as follows:

$$\Theta_e(s) = \Delta\phi \frac{s + \omega_n^2/K_v}{s^2 + 2\zeta\omega_n s + \omega_n^2} \tag{3.12}$$

Now we can normalize equations (3.9), (3.10) and (3.11) and each of them is related to the value of the damping factor.

If $\zeta < 1$, the two complex roots of the characteristic equation can be re-written as follows:

$$s_1 = a + jb = -\omega_n[\zeta - j(1 - \zeta^2)^{1/2}]$$

$$s_2 = a - jb = -\omega_n[\zeta + j(1 - \zeta^2)^{1/2}]$$

Identifying, we obtain

$$B = k + a = \zeta\omega_n$$

$$a = -\zeta\omega_n$$

$$b = \omega_n(1 - \zeta^2)^{1/2}$$

and, substituting these values into expression (3.9), we obtain

$$\theta_e(t) = \Delta\phi\, e^{-\zeta\omega t_n}\left\{\cos\left[\omega_n t(1-\zeta^2)^{1/2}\right] + \frac{\zeta}{(1-\zeta^2)^{1/2}}\sin\left[\omega_n t(1-\zeta^2)^{1/2}\right]\right\}$$

(3.13)

Setting ζ to 0 gives a double root:

$$\theta_e(t) = \Delta\phi\,(1+\omega_n t)\,e^{-\omega_n t}$$

(3.14)

When $\zeta > 1$ the two roots of the characteristic equation are real; then we have

$$B = k + a = \zeta\omega_n$$

$$a = -\zeta\omega_n$$

$$b' = \omega_n(\zeta^2 - 1)^{1/2}$$

from which we obtain

$$\theta_e(t) = \Delta\phi\, e^{-\zeta\omega_n t}\left\{\cosh\left[\omega_n t(\zeta^2-1)^{1/2}\right] + \frac{\zeta}{(\zeta^2-1)^{1/2}}\sinh\left[\omega_n t(\zeta^2-1)^{1/2}\right]\right\}$$

(3.15)

The curves illustrating the former equations are given in Fig. 3.3.

Angular frequency step applied to the reference input. Let $\Delta\omega$ be that step. Its phase ramp has the following Laplace transform: $\Delta\omega/s^2$.
    The expression for the phase error is

$$\Theta_e(s) = \Delta\omega\,\frac{s + 1/\tau}{s\,(s^2 + s/\tau + K_v/\tau)}$$

(3.16)

from which we obtain

$$\theta_e(0) = \lim_{s\to\infty} s\,\Delta\omega\,\frac{s + 1/\tau}{s\,(s^2 + s/\tau + K_v/\tau)} = 0$$

As for the study concerning the phase step, three cases exist, according to the roots of the characteristic equation.

FIRST CASE
Both roots are complex conjugate. Equation (3.16) takes the form

$$\frac{s + k}{s(s+\alpha)(s+\beta)}$$

From the Laplace transform pairs of the table in section A.2.7, we see that the inverse Laplace transform is

$$\frac{k}{\alpha\beta} + \frac{k-\alpha}{\alpha(\alpha-\beta)}\,e^{-\alpha t} + \frac{k-\beta}{\beta(\beta-\alpha)}\,e^{-\beta t}$$

(3.17)

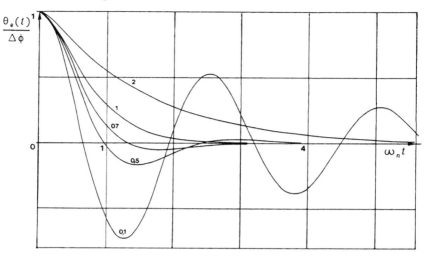

Fig. 3.3   Phase error due to a phase step (ζ is the parameter).

Using relations (3.8), and once again putting $B = k + a$, and combining them with expression (3.17), we obtain

$$\theta_e(t) = \Delta\omega\left[\frac{k}{a^2 + b^2} + \frac{B + jb}{2jb(a + jb)}e^{(a + jb)t} - \frac{B - jb}{2jb(a - jb)}e^{(a - jb)t}\right] \quad (3.18)$$

which, after some algebra manipulation, can be re-written in the following form:

$$\begin{aligned}\theta_e(t) = \frac{\Delta\omega}{a^2 + b^2}\Bigg\{ & B - a + \frac{ab - Bb}{b}\left[\frac{e^{(a + jb)t} + e^{(a - jb)t}}{2}\right] \\ & + \frac{b^2 + aB}{b}\left[\frac{e^{(a + jb)t} - e^{(a - jb)t}}{2j}\right]\Bigg\}\end{aligned}$$

Use of Euler's formulas yields

$$\theta_e(t) = \frac{\Delta\omega}{a^2 + b^2}\left\{B - a + \left[(a - B)\cos bt + \frac{b^2 + aB}{b}\sin bt\right]e^{at}\right\} \quad (3.19)$$

It can be checked that $\theta_e(0) = 0$.

SECOND CASE
The characteristic equation has a double root. The error is then given by

$$\Theta_e(s) = \frac{s + k}{s(s + \alpha)^2}$$

and its inverse Laplace transform is

$$\theta_e(t) = \Delta\omega\left[\frac{k}{\alpha^2} + \left(\frac{\alpha - k}{\alpha}t - \frac{k}{\alpha^2}\right)e^{-\alpha t}\right]$$

From equations (3.8) and as $b = 0$ and $k + a = B$, we then have

$$\theta_e(t) = \Delta\omega\left[\frac{B - a}{a^2}(1 - e^{at}) + t\frac{B}{a}e^{at}\right] \tag{3.20}$$

THIRD CASE
Both roots are real; we then find

$$\theta_e(t) = \frac{\Delta\omega}{a^2 - b'^2}\left\{B - a + \left[(a - B)\cosh b't + \frac{b'^2 + aB}{b'}\sinh b't\right]e^{at}\right\} \tag{3.21}$$

NORMALIZED EXPRESSIONS
Introducing the damping factor ζ and the natural angular frequency ω_n into equations (3.19), (3.20) and (3.21), we then have three cases.

1. $\zeta < 1$:

$$\theta_e(t) = \frac{2\zeta\,\Delta\omega}{\omega_n}\left(1 - \frac{e^{-\zeta\omega_n t}}{(1 - \zeta^2)^{1/2}}\left\{\left(\zeta - \frac{1}{2\zeta}\right)\sin\left[\omega_n t(1 - \zeta^2)^{1/2}\right]\right.\right.$$
$$\left.\left. + (1 - \zeta^2)^{1/2}\cos\left[\omega_n t(1 - \zeta^2)^{1/2}\right]\right\}\right) \tag{3.22}$$

2. $\zeta = 1$:

$$\theta_e(t) = \frac{2\,\Delta\omega}{\omega_n}\left[1 - e^{-\omega_n t}\left(1 + \frac{\omega_n t}{2}\right)\right] \tag{3.23}$$

3. $\zeta > 1$:

$$\theta_e(t) = \frac{2\zeta\,\Delta\omega}{\omega_n}\left(1 - \frac{e^{-\zeta\omega_n t}}{(\zeta^2 - 1)^{1/2}}\left\{\left(\zeta - \frac{1}{2\zeta}\right)\sinh\left[\omega_n t(\zeta^2 - 1)^{1/2}\right]\right.\right.$$
$$\left.\left. + (\zeta^2 - 1)^{1/2}\cosh\left[\omega_n t(\zeta^2 - 1)^{1/2}\right]\right\}\right) \tag{3.24}$$

Note. When $t \to \infty$, the three preceding functions tend to $2\zeta\,\Delta\omega/\omega_n$.

Since the parameters ζ and ω_n are defined by

$$\frac{1}{\tau} = 2\zeta\omega_n$$

$$\frac{k_v}{\tau} = \omega_n^2$$

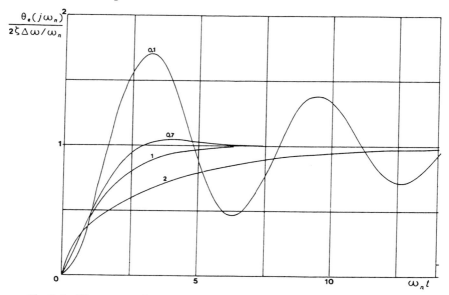

Fig. 3.4   Phase error due to an angular frequency step (ζ is the parameter).

we then have

$$K_v = \frac{\omega_n}{2\zeta}$$

The phase error tends to $\Delta\omega/K_v$, as calculated in section 3.2.2 (b). Figure 3.4 is a plot of the preceding functions.

(b)   Type 2 filter

Its schematic diagram is given in Fig. 2.3 together with its transfer function (equation (2.24b)). That is to say,

$$F(s) = \frac{1 + s\tau_2}{1 + s(\tau_1 + \tau_2)}$$

Substitution of this into equation (3.2) gives the transfer function of the phase error:

$$\Theta_e(s) = s\Theta_r(s)\frac{s + 1/(\tau_1 + \tau_2)}{s^2 + [(1 + K_v\tau_2)/(\tau_1 + \tau_2)]s + K_v/(\tau_1 + \tau_2)} \qquad (3.25)$$

Let us, once again, use the damping factor and the natural frequency, defined as follows:

$$2\zeta\omega_n = \frac{1 + K_v\tau_2}{\tau_1 + \tau_2}$$

$$\omega_n^2 = \frac{K_v}{\tau_1 + \tau_2}$$

Substituting into equation (3.25), and setting $\Theta_n(s) = \dfrac{\Delta\phi}{s}$ we have

$$\Theta_e(s) = \Delta\phi \frac{s + \omega_n^2/K_v}{s^2 + 2\zeta\omega_n s + \omega_n^2} \qquad (3.26)$$

If we compare equation (3.12) with the preceding one, we note that they are identical. Therefore, all the results regarding transient behaviour owing to the application of phase or frequency steps are the same as those for a type 1 filter.

(c) Type 3 filter

The schematic diagram is given in Fig. 2.3. Its use in PLL applications is very popular since performances are very good. Moreover, it is quite simple to calculate its characteristics.

The filter transfer function is given in equation (2.47). Substituting it into expression (3.2), gives the phase error:

$$\Theta_e(s) = \Theta_r(s) \frac{s}{s^2 + K_v(\tau_2/\tau_1)s + K_v/\tau_1} \qquad (3.27)$$

Phase step applied to the reference intput. The Laplace transform of the phase step is $\Delta\phi/s$ and the equation of the phase error is given by

$$\Theta_e(s) = \Delta\phi \frac{s^2}{s^2 + K_v(\tau_2/\tau_1)s + K_v/\tau_1} \qquad (3.28)$$

As for the other three filters, three cases are involved.

FIRST CASE
Roots are complex conjugate. The second member of equation (3.28) is as follows:

$$\frac{s}{(s + \alpha)(s + \beta)}$$

The roots being

$$s_1 = -\alpha = a + jb$$

$$s_2 = -\beta = a - jb$$

the inverse Laplace transform is then

$$\theta_e(t) = \Delta\phi \frac{(a+jb)e^{(a+jb)t} + (-a+jb)e^{(a-jb)t}}{2jb}$$

Using Euler's formulas, this can be written

$$\theta_e(t) = \frac{\Delta\phi}{b}(a \sin bt + b \cos bt)e^{at} \tag{3.29}$$

SECOND CASE

The root is double. The Laplace transform of the phase error is given by

$$\Theta_e(s) = \Delta\Phi \frac{s}{(s+\alpha)^2}$$

and the inverse Laplace transform is of the form

$$(1 - \alpha t)e^{-\alpha t}$$

Since the root is equal to

$$s_{12} = -\alpha = a$$

the phase error equation is

$$\theta_e(t) = \Delta\phi(at + 1)e^{at} \tag{3.30}$$

THIRD CASE

The roots are real and this case can be deduced from the case of complex roots by changing sin into sinh, cos into cosh and b into b'; we then have

$$\theta_e(t) = \frac{\Delta\phi}{b}(a \sinh b't + b' \cosh b't)e^{at} \tag{3.31}$$

Substituting the variables ζ and ω_n into the three preceding equations, we see that there are three cases.

1. $\zeta < 1$:

$$\theta_e(t) = \Delta\phi\left[\cos \omega_n t(1-\zeta^2)^{1/2} - \frac{\zeta}{(1-\zeta^2)^{1/2}}\sin \omega_n t(1-\zeta^2)^{1/2}e^{-\zeta\omega_n t}\right] \tag{3.32}$$

2. $\zeta = 1$:

$$\theta_e(t) = \Delta\phi(1 - \omega_n t)e^{-\omega_n t} \tag{3.33}$$

3. $\zeta > 1$:

$$\theta_e(t) = \Delta\phi\left[\cosh \omega_n t(\zeta^2-1)^{1/2} - \frac{\zeta}{(\zeta^2-1)^{1/2}}\sinh \omega_n t(\zeta^2-1)^{1/2}e^{-\zeta\omega_n t}\right]$$
$$\tag{3.34}$$

Figure 3.5 is a plot of the preceding functions.

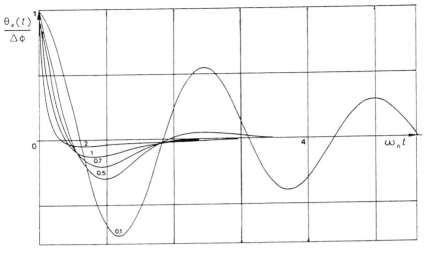

Fig. 3.5 Phase error due to a phase step (ζ is the parameter).

Angular frequency step applied to the reference input. Let $\Delta\omega/s^2$ be the Laplace transform of the angular frequency step. The equation for the phase error is of the form

$$\Theta_{\mathrm{e}}(s) = \frac{\Delta\omega}{s^2 + k_{\mathrm{v}}(\tau_2/\tau_1)s + (K_{\mathrm{v}}/\tau_1)}$$

FIRST CASE
The two roots of the characteristic equation are complex conjugate. The phase error equation is of the form

$$\frac{\mathrm{e}^{-\alpha t} - \mathrm{e}^{-\beta t}}{\beta - \alpha}$$

With our usual notation regarding the roots, the phase error equation is as follows:

$$\theta_{\mathrm{e}}(t) = \Delta\omega \frac{\mathrm{e}^{(a+jb)t} - \mathrm{e}^{(a-jb)t}}{2jb}$$

$$\theta_{\mathrm{e}}(t) = \frac{\Delta\omega}{b} \sin bt \, \mathrm{e}^{at} \tag{3.35}$$

SECOND CASE
The root of the characteristic equation is double. The equation of the phase error is found to be

$$\frac{\Delta\omega}{(s+\alpha)^2}$$

and its inverse Laplace transform is

$$t\,e^{-\alpha t}$$

Therefore, the phase error is given by

$$\theta_e(t) = \Delta\omega\, t\, e^{at} \tag{3.36}$$

THIRD CASE
The two roots are real. We can deduce the result from the complex root case. We then have

$$\theta_e(t) = \frac{\Delta\omega}{b'} \sinh b't\, e^{at} \tag{3.37}$$

NORMALIZED EXPRESSIONS
They are obtained using the following variables:

$$a = -\zeta\omega_n$$
$$b = \omega_n(1 - \zeta^2)^{1/2}$$

The preceding results then have the following, more common form.

1. $\zeta < 1$ gives

$$\theta_e(t) = \frac{\Delta\omega}{\omega_n(1 - \zeta^2)^{1/2}} \sin \omega_n t (1 - \zeta^2)^{1/2}\, e^{-\zeta\omega_n t} \tag{3.38}$$

2. For $\zeta = 1$ we find

$$\theta_e(t) = \Delta\omega t\, e^{-\omega_n t} \tag{3.39}$$

3. For $\zeta > 1$ we have

$$\theta_e(t) = \frac{\Delta\omega}{\omega_n(\zeta^2 - 1)^{1/2}} \sinh \omega_n t (\zeta^2 - 1)^{1/2}\, e^{-\omega_n t \zeta} \tag{3.40}$$

Note. The preceding equations show that the phase error due to an angular frequency step is zero after an infinite time when in section 3.2.2(b) we gave $\Delta\omega/AK_v$. This discrepancy is due to the fact that the transfer function of the filter used in the previous calculation assumed that the gain of the operational amplifier was infinite.

The three phase error functions are plotted in Fig. 3.6.

(d) Type 4 filter

The filter's schematic diagram is given in Fig. 2.3.
    Its transfer function is given by equation (2.58). Substituting it into equa-

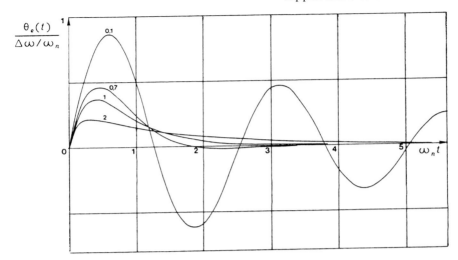

Fig. 3.6 Phase error due to an angular frequency step (ζ is the parameter).

tion (3.2) gives the expression of the phase error:

$$\Theta_e(s) = \Theta_r(s) \frac{(1/\tau_3 + s) s^2}{s^3 + (1/\tau_3)s^2 + (K_v \tau_2/\tau_1\tau_3) s + K_v/\tau_1\tau_3} \tag{3.41}$$

Phase step applied to the reference input. Let $\Delta\phi/s$ be the Laplace transform of the step. It will generate a phase error of the form

$$\Theta_e(s) = \Delta\phi \frac{s(1/\tau_3 + s)}{s^3 + (1/\tau_3)s^2 + (K_v \tau_2/\tau_1\tau_3) s + K_v/\tau_1\tau_3} \tag{3.42}$$

FIRST CASE
The characteristic equation has two complex roots and one real root. The phase error is then

$$\frac{s(f+s)}{(s+\alpha)(s+\beta)(s+\gamma)}$$

and its inverse Laplace transform is

$$\frac{(\alpha^2 - f\alpha)e^{-\alpha t}}{(\beta - \alpha)(\gamma - \alpha)} + \frac{(\beta^2 - f\beta)e^{-\beta t}}{(\alpha - \beta)(\gamma - \beta)} + \frac{(\gamma^2 - f\gamma)e^{-\gamma t}}{(\alpha - \gamma)(\beta - \gamma)} \tag{3.43}$$

Let

$$s_1 = \alpha = a + jb$$
$$s_2 = -\beta = a - jb \tag{3.44}$$
$$s_3 = c = -\gamma$$

be the expressions of the roots.

Substituting them in equation (3.42), and after a long calculation, we find

$$\theta_e(t) = \frac{\Delta\phi}{(a-c)^2+b^2}\, e^{at} \left\{ \left[\frac{a}{b}(a+f)(a-c)+b(a+b+f) \right] \sin bt \right.$$

$$\left. + [(a-c)^2+b^2-c(c+f)]\cos bt \right\} + \frac{c(c+f)\Delta\phi}{(a-c)^2+b^2}\, e^{ct} \qquad (3.45)$$

As can be seen, there are two main terms. One is an exponentially decreasing sine function which looks as though it were obtained with a second-order system; the second one is a decreasing exponential function. The influence of this second term will be important or not depending on the value of c.

SECOND CASE

If one of the roots is double, and therefore real, we obtain, for the phase error, the following expression:

$$\frac{s(f+s)}{(\alpha+s)^2(\gamma+s)}$$

The inverse Laplace transform is

$$(L+Mt)e^{-\alpha t}+Ce^{-\gamma t} \qquad (3.46)$$

where

$$L = 1 - \frac{c(c+f)}{(a-c)^2}$$

$$M = \frac{a(a+f)}{(a-c)}$$

$$C = \frac{c(c+f)}{(a-c)^2}$$

Then, we deduce the phase error function:

$$\theta_e(t) = \Delta\phi \left[\frac{a^2-2ac-cf}{(a-c)^2}\, e^{at} + \frac{a+f}{a-c}\, t e^{at} + \frac{c(c+f)}{(a-c)^2}\, e^{ct} \right] \qquad (3.47)$$

THIRD CASE

The three roots are real. We write them as follows:

$$s_1 = -\alpha$$

$$s_2 = -\beta$$

$$s_3 = -\gamma$$

This allows us to use expression (3.43), from which the phase error can be calculated; we find

$$\theta_e(t) = \frac{(\alpha^2 - f\alpha)e^{-\alpha t}}{(\beta - \alpha)(\gamma - \alpha)} + \frac{(\beta^2 - f\beta)e^{-\beta t}}{(\alpha - \beta)(\gamma - \beta)} + \frac{(\gamma^2 - f\gamma)e^{-\gamma t}}{(\alpha - \gamma)(\beta - \gamma)} \qquad (3.48)$$

Angular frequency step applied to the reference input. Let $\Delta\omega/s^2$ be the Laplace transform of the angular frequency step. We deduce the resulting phase error whose expression is

$$\Theta_e(s) = \Delta\omega \frac{(1/\tau_3 + s)}{s^3 + (1/\tau_3)s^2 + (K_v\tau_2/\tau_1\tau_3)s + K_v/\tau_1\tau_3} \qquad (3.49)$$

FIRST CASE

The characteristic equation (3.49) has two complex conjugate roots. Therefore, the phase error can be written in the following form:

$$\frac{f + s}{(s + \alpha)(s + \beta)(s + \gamma)}$$

Its inverse Laplace transform is

$$\frac{f - \alpha}{(\beta - \alpha)(\gamma - \alpha)} e^{-\alpha t} + \frac{f - \beta}{(\alpha - \beta)(\gamma - \beta)} e^{-\beta t} + \frac{f - \gamma}{(\alpha - \gamma)(\beta - \gamma)} e^{-\gamma t}$$

Substituting relations (3.44) into the preceding equation and after a long calculation, we find that the phase error, in the time domain, is given by the following relationship:

$$\theta_e(t) = \frac{\Delta\omega}{(a - c)^2 + b^2} \left\{ -(f + c)\cos bt + \left[\frac{(f + a)(a - c)}{b} + b \right] \sin bt \right\} e^{at}$$

$$+ \frac{(f + c)\Delta\omega\, e^{ct}}{(a - c)^2 + b^2} \qquad (3.50)$$

SECOND CASE

A root of the characteristic equation is double, necessary real, and there is also the third root; the phase error equation can be written as follows:

$$\frac{s + f}{(s + \alpha)^2(s + \beta)}$$

and the inverse Laplace transform is

$$\frac{f - \beta}{(\alpha - \beta)^2} e^{-\beta t} + \left[\frac{f - \alpha}{\beta - \alpha} t + \frac{\beta - f}{(\beta - \alpha)^2} \right] e^{-\alpha t} \qquad (3.51)$$

the roots being

$$\alpha = -a \text{ (double root)}$$

$$\beta = -c$$

Equation (3.51) is written as

$$\theta_e(t) = \frac{\Delta\omega(f+c)}{(a-c)^2}e^{bt} + \frac{\Delta\omega}{(a-c)^2}[(f+a)(a-c)t - (c+f)]e^{at} \qquad (3.52)$$

THIRD CASE

The three roots of the characteristic equation are real, in which case the inverse Laplace transform has the following form:

$$\frac{f-\alpha}{(\beta-\alpha)(\gamma-\alpha)}e^{-\alpha t} + \frac{f-\beta}{(\alpha-\beta)(\gamma-\beta)}e^{-\beta t} + \frac{f-\gamma}{(\alpha-\gamma)(\beta-\gamma)}e^{-\gamma t}$$

and the phase error is

$$\theta_e(t) = \frac{f-\alpha}{(\beta-\alpha)(\gamma-\alpha)}e^{-\alpha t} + \frac{f-\beta}{(\alpha-\beta)(\gamma-\beta)}e^{-\beta t} + \frac{f-\gamma}{(\alpha-\gamma)(\beta-\gamma)}e^{-\gamma t}$$
$$(3.53)$$

We saw in section 2.5.2 that it was possible to simplify drastically the calculations of such a system by choosing K_v so that the straight lines from the origin whose slopes are equal to $\pm\zeta$ be tangential to the root loci in the s-plane. We saw that the real root (the other two are complex conjugate) is equal to $-\omega_n$.

Let us replace in equations (3.45) and (3.50)

$$f = \omega_n(1 + 2\zeta)$$
$$a = -\omega_n\zeta$$
$$b = (1 - \zeta^2)^{1/2}\omega_n$$
$$c = -\omega_n$$

We find that the phase error due to a phase step is given by

$$\theta_e(t) = \frac{\Delta\phi}{2(1-\zeta)}\{[-\zeta^2 + 1 + (1-\zeta^2)^{1/2}]\sin[\omega_n t(1-\zeta^2)^{1/2}]$$

$$+ 2\cos[\omega_n t(1-\zeta^2)^{1/2}]e^{-\zeta\omega_n t} - \frac{\zeta\Delta\phi}{1-\zeta}e^{-\omega_n t} \qquad (3.54)$$

and the phase error due to an angular frequency step is given by

$$\theta_e(t) = \frac{\Delta\omega_n}{2\omega_n(1-\zeta)}\{(1-\zeta^2)^{1/2}\sin[\omega_n t(1-\zeta^2)^{1/2}]$$

$$- \zeta\cos[\omega_n t(1-\zeta^2)^{1/2}]\}e^{-\zeta\omega_n t} + \frac{\zeta\Delta\omega}{\omega_n(1-\zeta)}e^{-\omega_n t} \qquad (3.55)$$

Figure 3.7 is a plot of equation (3.45) corresponding to a damping factor equal

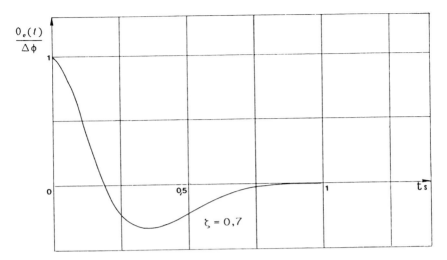

Fig. 3.7 Phase error due to a phase step in a stable system.

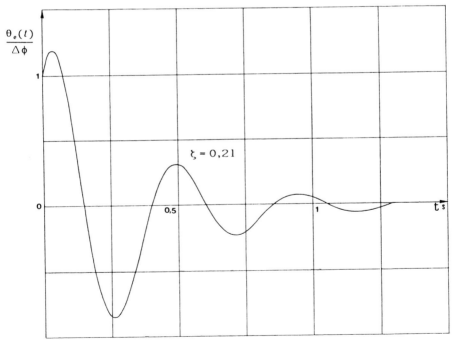

Fig. 3.8 Phase error due to a phase step in an unstable stable system.

to 0.7. Parameters defining this function are

$$a = -5.85$$
$$b = +5.89$$
$$c = -8.31$$
$$f = +20.00$$

Figure 3.8 is a plot of equation (3.45) corresponding to a damping factor equal to 0.21. Parameters defining this function are

$$a = -2.93$$
$$b = +13.83$$
$$c = -14.14$$
$$f = +20.00$$

These two examples correspond to the stability study of a motor. The first one was studied in section 2.5.3. The second one is related to a motor with a filter whose damping does not ensure good stability. It is worth noting that the curve of Fig. 3.8 has a bound on the phase error as $\theta_e(t) > \Delta\phi$. This behaviour is never observed in a second-order system.

4

Response to a sinusoidal excitation

In Chapter 3, we studied the response to some impulse excitations in order to test the accuracy and the stability of a PLL system.

The ability of the PLL to self-tune to the centre frequency of the reference carrier makes it the ideal solution for frequency modulation (FM) and amplitude modulation (AM) and demodulation. Owing to the importance of these applications, we shall study in this chatper the response to a sinusoidal driving function. This response can be deduced from the transfer functions we saw in the preceding chapters.

4.1 PRELIMINARY REMARKS

In Chapter 1, we saw that we could obtain, at the filter output, a voltage proportional to the instantaneous amplitude modulation signal.

If we want the demodulation to be distortion free, the filters which are to be used must not present overshoots of $\pm 3\,\text{dB}$ within the frequency range of the modulating signal. This implies that the amplitude voltage at the output filter must be practically constant versus the modulating frequency when the amplitude of the modulating signal itself is constant.

Moreover, the phase error due to the sinusoidal PC must not be exceeded to prevent unlock. This limit, for a given frequency deviation, depends on the damping factor and on the natural frequency of the system. Theoretically, this limit should not exceed 90°. According to the literature [2, 5] in order to be safe, as far as noise is concerned, it is fixed at 57° (1 rad).

The preceding limit should also ensure that the sinusoidal PC works in its linear region which is the condition for the transfer function to be valid. A lower limit is also found [6], which is fixed at about 30° (0.5 rad).

4.2 SINUSOIDAL FM MODULATION

4.2.1 Amplitude and phase at the filter output

Let

$$e(t) = E_e \cos\left(\omega_0 t + \frac{\Delta\omega}{\omega_m}\sin\omega_m t\right)$$

be the equation of an FM signal.

We shall suppose that $\Delta\omega/\omega_m$ is small enough ($< 1/2$ rad) so that only the linear region of the PC need be used. Thus, in such a case, the results using the transfer functions remain valid.

From the preceding equation we obtain the phase reference

$$\theta_r(t) = \frac{\Delta\omega}{\omega_m} \sin \omega_m t$$

which can be re-written, using complex notation, as follows:

$$\Theta_r(j\omega_m) = \frac{\Delta\omega}{\omega_m} e^{j\omega_m t} \tag{4.1}$$

The phase, $\theta_1(t)$, of the oscillator, in steady-state conditions, is also sinusoidal, its angular frequency being ω_m.

Let $V_f(s)$ be the Laplace transform of the amplitude v_f at the output of the filter. From equation (2.18) we have

$$V_f(s) = \frac{s}{K_0} \Theta_r(s) T(s) \tag{4.2}$$

Replacing s with $j\omega_m$, and substituting $\Theta_r(j\omega_m)$ from equation (4.1) into equation (4.2), we find

$$K_0 V_f(j\omega_m) = j \Delta\omega\, e^{j\omega_m t} T(j\omega_m) \tag{4.3}$$

and

$$\frac{V_f(j\omega_m)}{\Delta\omega/K_0} = j e^{j\omega_m t} T(j\omega_m) \tag{4.4}$$

Thus

$$\frac{|V_f(j\omega_m)|}{\Delta\omega/K_0} = |T(j\omega_m)| \tag{4.5}$$

and

$$\Phi(j\omega_m) = \frac{\pi}{2} + \arg|T(j\omega_m)| \tag{4.6}$$

4.2.2   Steady-state peak phase error

Under steady-state conditions, and using complex notation, the phase error has the following form:

$$\Theta_e(j\omega_m) = \rho_e e^{j(\omega_m t + \phi_e)} \tag{4.7}$$

Let us, in equation (3.2), substitute s with $j\omega_m$. We then find

$$\Theta_e(j\omega_m) = \Theta_r(j\omega_m) \frac{j\omega_m}{j\omega_m + K_v F(j\omega_m)}$$

$$= \Theta_r(j\omega_m)[1 - T(j\omega_m)] \tag{4.8}$$

Substituting $\Theta_r(j\omega_m)$ and $\Theta_e(j\omega_m)$ from equations (4.1) and (4.7) into (4.8), we obtain

$$\Theta_e(j\omega_m) = \rho_e e^{j(\omega_m t + \phi_e)} = \frac{\Delta\omega}{\omega_m} e^{j\omega_m t}[1 - T(j\omega_m)]$$

Therefore

$$\rho_e = |\Theta_e(j\omega_m)| = \frac{\Delta\omega}{\omega_m}|1 - T(j\omega_m)|$$

$$\Phi_e = \arg|1 - T(j\omega_m)|$$

(4.9)

and

$$\frac{|\Theta_e(j\omega_m)|}{\Delta\omega/\omega_n} = \left|\frac{1 - T(j\omega_m)}{\omega_m/\omega_n}\right|$$

(4.10)

4.3   APPLICATION TO THE DIFFERENT LOOPS

4.3.1   First-order loop

In this case we have $|F(j\omega_m)| = 1$.

(a)   Amplitude at the filter output

In equation (4.5), let us replace $|T(j\omega_m)|$ with

$$\frac{K_v}{(s^2 + K_v^2)^{1/2}} = \frac{\omega_n}{(\omega_m^2 + \omega_n^2)^{1/2}}$$

setting $\omega_m/\omega_n = x$, we obtain

$$\frac{|V_f(j\omega_m)|}{\Delta\omega/K_0} = \frac{1}{(1 + x^2)^{1/2}}$$

(4.11)

Let us plot equation (4.11), putting

$$20\log\frac{|V_f(j\omega_m)|}{\Delta\omega/K_0}$$

as the ordinate and $x = \omega_m/\omega_n$ as the abscissa: this has been done in Fig. 4.1. We can see that the loop has the same characteristics as first-order filter whose corner frequency $(-3\,\text{dB})$ is $\omega_n/2\pi$ and whose centre frequency is $\omega_0/2\pi$ (Fig. 4.2).

If such a circuit is used for FM demodulation purposes, the absence of filter will let additional frequencies pass. Therefore, it will be necessary to add one outside the loop.

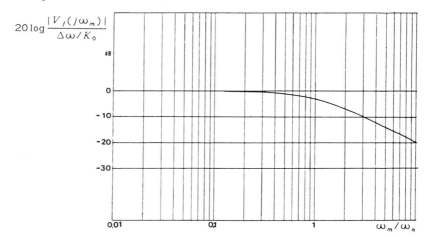

Fig. 4.1   Frequency response of a first-order loop.

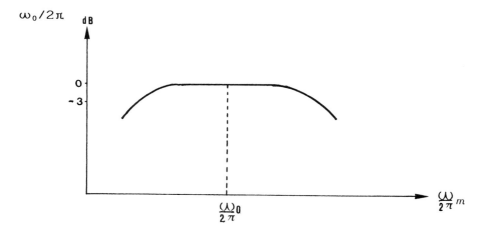

Fig. 4.2   Filter bandwidth centred on $\omega_0/2\pi$.

(b)   Steady-state peak phase error

Equation (4.10) represents the expression of the steady-state peak phase error. Following a similar calculation as in the preceding section we find

$$\frac{|\Theta_{\mathrm{e}}(j\omega_{\mathrm{m}})|}{\Delta\omega/\omega_{\mathrm{n}}} = \frac{1}{(1+x^2)^{1/2}} \tag{4.12}$$

This function is the same as that related to the amplitude V_f.

If $\Delta\omega$ and ω_n are given, from equation (4.12) we can calculate $|\Theta_e(j\omega_m)|$ and then we can check that the calculated value does not exceed 1 rad, in order to be sure that the system will not unlock. Then we make sure that $\omega_m \leqslant \omega_n$, that is to say $x \leqslant 1$, and we calculate the angular frequency limit deviation:

$$\Delta\omega < \sqrt{2}\omega_n$$

4.3.2 Second-order loop

(a) Type 1 filter

Amplitude at the filter output. Replacing s with $j\omega_m$ in equation (2.21), and then replacing it in equation (4.5) and setting $x = \omega_m/\omega_n$ gives

$$\frac{|V_f(j\omega_m)|}{\Delta\omega/K_0} = \frac{1}{[(1-x^2)^2 + 4\zeta^2 x^2]^{1/2}} \tag{4.13}$$

Before plotting the normalized amplitude

$$\frac{|V_f(j\omega_m)|}{\Delta\omega/K_0}$$

as a function of the normalized angular frequency $x = \omega_m/\omega_n$, let us determine the angular frequency corresponding to -3 dB and the angular frequency related to its maximum.

The angular frequency, ω_{-3dB}, can be calculated as

$$\frac{|V_f(j\omega_m)|}{\Delta\omega/K_0} = \frac{1}{[(1-x^2)^2 + 4\zeta^2 x^2]^{1/2}} = \frac{\sqrt{2}}{2} \tag{4.14}$$

Squaring both members of the preceding equation, we obtain

$$\frac{1}{(1-x^2)^2 + 4\zeta^2 x^2} = \frac{1}{2}$$

from which we have the following fourth-degree equation:

$$x^4 + 2x^2(2\zeta^2 - 1) - 1 = 0$$

The acceptable root is

$$x = \{1 - 2\zeta^2 + [(1 - 2\zeta^2)^2 + 1]^{1/2}\}^{1/2}$$

thus

$$\omega_{-3dB} = \omega_n\{1 - 2\zeta^2 + [(1 - 2\zeta^2)^2 + 1]^{1/2}\}^{1/2} \tag{4.15}$$

As we can see, the angular frequency only depends on the damping factor ζ. When $\zeta = \sqrt{2}/2$ the corner angular frequency, ω_{-3dB}, is equal to ω_n.

The magnitude

$$\frac{|V_f(j\omega_m)|}{\Delta\omega/K_0}$$

reaches a maximum when the expression

$$[(1 - x^2)^2 + 4\zeta^2 x^2]^{1/2}$$

is at a minimum. Squaring it, taking the derivative with respect to x, and then setting it equal to 0, gives

$$-(1 - x^2) + 2\zeta^2 = 0$$
$$x^2 = 1 - 2\zeta^2$$
$$\omega_m = \omega_n(1 - 2\zeta^2)^{1/2}$$

This maximum is only possible when

$$2\zeta^2 < 1$$
$$\zeta < 0.707$$

This value ensures the lowest distortion when FM demodulation is carried out. At the same time, this allows a bandwidth equal to $\pm\omega_n$. For this reason, it is used in many projects.

Figure 4.3 is a plot of the normalized amplitude at the output of the filter when ζ is a parameter. We can see the strong influence of the damping factor

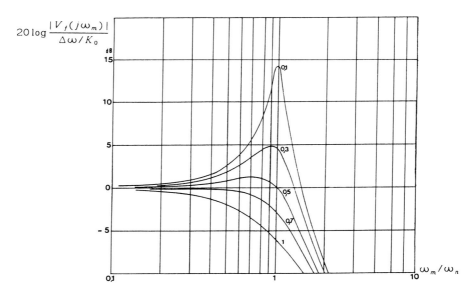

Fig. 4.3 Frequency response with a filter of type 1.

whose value, when low, causes the amplitude to increase, giving rise to a certain instability in the loop. A high value of the same factor will delay the system.

A good balance can be achieved with a value around 0.7. This value is also justified from the considerations seen above.

Steady-state peak phase error. From expression (2.21), we calculate $1 - T(s)$ and we find

$$1 - T(s) = \frac{s^2 + 2\zeta\omega_n s}{s^2 + 2\zeta\omega_n s + \omega_n^2}$$

Next we replace s with $j\omega_m$, set $x = \omega_m/\omega_n$ and according to equation (4.10), we obtain

$$\frac{|\Theta_e(j\omega_m)|}{(\Delta\omega/\omega_n)} = \frac{(x^2 + 4\zeta^2)^{1/2}}{[(1 - x^2)^2 + 4\zeta^2 x^2]^{1/2}} \qquad (4.16)$$

We have plotted, in Fig. 4.4, the expression

$$\frac{|\Theta_e(j\omega_m)|}{\Delta\omega/\omega_n}$$

as a function of the normalized variable x, and with the damping factor ζ as a parameter.

This plot is of great interest when FM transmission is used to determine the

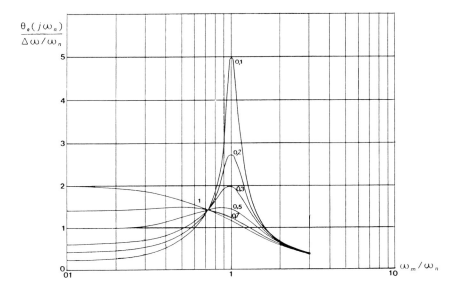

Fig. 4.4 Steady-state peak phase error (type 1 filter).

natural angular frequency ω_n, compatible with the frequency deviation $\Delta\omega$ preventing the PLL unlock. In section 4.3.2(c) we propose a practical exercise on how to use Fig. 4.4.

(b)   Type 2 filter

Amplitude at the filter output. Let us in equation (4.5) substitute $|T(j\omega_m)|$ with equation (2.32) where we set $s = j\omega_m$. Next we normalize the angular frequency setting $x = \omega_m/\omega_n$ and we find

$$\frac{|V_f(j\omega_m)|}{\Delta\omega/K_0} = \left\{ \frac{x^2(2\zeta - \omega_n/K_v)^2 + 1}{[(1 - x^2)^2 + 4\zeta^2 x^2]^{1/2}} \right\}^{1/2} \tag{4.17}$$

Before plotting the normalized amplitude against $x = \omega_m/\omega_n$, let us determine the corner angular frequency.

The angular frequency, ω_{-3dB}, is calculated as follows:

$$\frac{|V_f(j\omega_m)|}{\Delta\omega/K_0} = \frac{[x^2(2\zeta - \omega_n/K_v)^2 + 1]^{1/2}}{[(1 - x^2)^2 + 4\zeta^2 x^2]^{1/2}} = \frac{\sqrt{2}}{2} \tag{4.18}$$

squaring the two sides of equation (4.18), we obtain

$$\frac{x^2(2\zeta - \omega_n/K_v)^2 + 1}{(1 - x^2)^2 + 4\zeta^2 x^2} = \frac{1}{2}$$

which can be re-written as

$$x^4 + x^2 \left[4\zeta^2 - 2 - 2\left(2\zeta - \frac{\omega_n}{K_v} \right)^2 \right] - 1 = 0 \tag{4.19}$$

whose acceptable root is

$$x = \frac{\omega_{-3dB}}{\omega_n} = \left[1 + 2\zeta^2 + \frac{\omega_n}{K_n}\left(\frac{\omega_n}{K_v} - 4\zeta\right) + \left\{ 1 + \left[1 + 2\zeta^2 + \frac{\omega_n}{K_v}\left(\frac{\omega_n}{K_v} - 4\zeta\right) \right]^2 \right\}^{1/2} \right]^{1/2} \tag{4.20}$$

Setting

$$a = 1 + 2\zeta^2 + \frac{\omega_n}{K_v}\left(\frac{\omega_n}{K_v} - 4\zeta\right)$$

facilitates the calculation and we find

$$\omega_{-3dB} = \omega_n[a + (a^2 + 1)^{1/2}]^{1/2}$$

As the condition $\omega_n \ll K_v$ is fulfilled most of the time, we can simplify the final result and write

$$\omega_{-3dB} = \omega_n\{1 + 2\zeta^2 + [(1 + 2\zeta^2)^2 + 1]^{1/2}\}^{1/2}$$

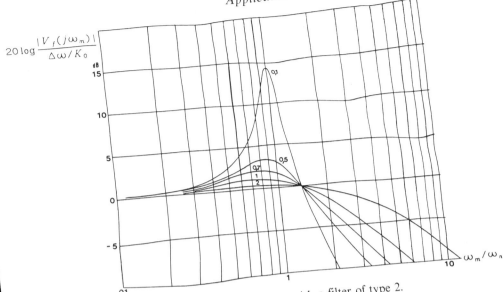

Fig. 4.5　Frequency response with a filter of type 2.

For instance, with $\zeta = \sqrt{2}/2$, we find

$$\omega_{-3\mathrm{dB}} = 2.06\,\omega_n$$

The Bode diagram is plotted in Fig. 4.5, with

$$20\log\frac{|V_f(j\omega_m)|}{\Delta\omega/K_0}$$

on the ordinate and ω_m/ω_n on the abscissa, the damping factor ζ being the parameter. We have supposed that $\omega_n/K_v = 0$.

This plot is to be compared with the plot in Fig. 4.3. We can see that for a value of the damping factor $\geqslant 0.7$, no bouncing exists with the filter of type 1, and therefore the system is more stable with that type of filter. Remember that Fig. 4.5 corresponds to a large value of the gain K_v. Therefore, we should expect the system to be less stable.

Steady-state phase error. From equation (2.32) we calculate $1 - T(s)$, and we find

$$1 - T(s) = \frac{s(s + \omega_n^2/K_v)}{s^2 + 2\zeta\omega_n s + \omega_n^2} \tag{4.21}$$

Then, replacing s with $j\omega_m$ in equation (4.21), and substituting the result in equation (4.10), yields

$$\frac{|\Theta_e(j\omega_m)|}{\Delta\omega/\omega_n} = \frac{(x^2 + \omega_n^2/K_v^2)^{1/2}}{[(1-x^2)^2 + 4\zeta^2 x^2]^{1/2}} \tag{4.22}$$

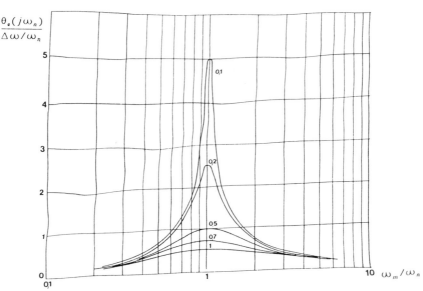

Fig. 4.6   Steady-state peak phase error (type 2 filter).

Equation (4.22) is plotted in Fig. 4.6 for different values of the damping factor.

There is a symmetrical axis, whose equation is $x = 1$. Such a symmetrical axis is not present when a filter of type 1 is used (Fig. 4.4).

Concerning the filter of type 2, the results given so far correspond to a large loop gain, which can be obtained by means of an amplifier. Nevertheless, we must assume that the amplifier has no poles within the application frequency range. Otherwise, the loop will no longer be of the second order.

As we shall see in the next section, the results will be very close to those obtained with a filter of type 3.

(c)   *Filter of type 3*

Comparing the closed-loop transfer functions $T(s)$ represented by equations (2.32) and (2.50), it can be *seen* that they are identical when, in equation (2.50), we set $\omega_n/K_v = 0$. Therefore, all the results related to the filter of type 2 are also valid for the filter of type 3 provided that the above condition is true and with

$$K_v \frac{\tau_2}{\tau_1} = 2\zeta\omega_n$$

$$\frac{K_v}{\tau_1} = \omega_n^2$$

Amplitude at the filter output. If in equation (4.17), we set $\omega_n/K_v = 0$, we obtain we obtain

$$\frac{|V_f(j\omega_m)|}{\Delta\omega/K_0} = \left\{\frac{2\zeta x^2 + 1}{[(1 - x^2)^2 + 4\zeta^2 x^2]^{1/2}}\right\}^{1/2} \tag{4.23}$$

from which we obtain the corner angular frequency (-3 dB):

$$\omega_{-3\mathrm{dB}} = \omega_n\{1 + 2\zeta^2 + [(1 + 2\zeta^2)^2 + 1]^{1/2}\}^{1/2}$$

Steady-state phase error. Setting the same condition as above, $\omega_n/K_v = 0$, in equation (4.22) gives

$$\frac{|\Theta_e(j\omega_m)|}{\Delta\omega/\omega_n} = \frac{x}{[(1 - x^2)^2 + 4\zeta^2 x^2]^{1/2}} \tag{4.24}$$

Because we set $\omega_n/K_v = 0$ plots corresponding to equations (4.23) and (4.24) are not given since they are the same as those of Fig. 4.5 and Fig. 4.6.

Numerical example. Let 15 000 Hz be the centre frequency intended to transmit in FM a set of telemetry channels.

The characteristics of the modulating signal are

$$\Delta f = 1000 \text{ Hz}$$
$$f_m = 250 \text{ Hz}$$

Let us determine the natural frequency. To start with we shall select 250 Hz. We then have

$$\frac{\omega_m}{\omega_n} = \frac{f_m}{f_n} = 1$$

If from Fig. 4.6 we select the curve corresponding to $\zeta = 0.7$, the peak phase error is 0.7. Since we know the ratio $\Delta f/f_n$ to be equal to 4, we can calculate the phase error $|\Theta_e(j\omega_m)|$; we find $4 \times 0.7 = 2.8$ rad. This is unacceptable since it will unlock the loop.

Let us try a higher value, for instance $f_n = 500$ Hz. We then have, on the same figure and on the same curve, for an abscissa of 0.5, an ordinate of about 0.5. Since the ratio $\Delta f/f_n$ is now equal to 2, we find 1 rad (57°), which is an acceptable value.

4.3.3 Third-order loop

In order to reduce the complexity of the calculations, we shall examine the case, already studied, where the real root of the characteristic equation is equal to ω_n. Then the equation is as follows

$$(s + \omega_n)(s^2 + 2\zeta\omega_n s + \omega_n^2) = 0$$

(a)   Amplitude at the filter output

In equation (2.59) for the closed-loop transfer function let us substitute τ_3, τ_2 and τ_1 from, respectively, relations (2.81), (2.82) and (2.83). Then setting $s = j\omega_m$, we obtain

$$T(j\omega_n) = \frac{\omega_n^2[\omega_n + j\omega_m(1 + 2\zeta)]}{(\omega_n + j\omega_m)(-\omega_m^2 + 2j\omega_n\omega_m\zeta + \omega_n^2)} \qquad (4.25)$$

Setting $x = \omega_m/\omega_n$ in equation (4.25) and then calculating its magnitude, we have the filter output amplitude:

$$\frac{|V_f(j\omega_m)|}{\Delta\omega/K_0} = |T(j\omega_m)| = \frac{[1 + (1 + 2\zeta)^2x^2]^{1/2}}{(1 + x^2)^{1/2}[(1 - x^2)^2 + 4\zeta^2x^2]^{1/2}} \qquad (4.26)$$

Let us now plot the filter output amplitude versus the normalized angular frequency with ζ as a parameter (Fig. 4.7).

It is worth comparing the curves of the amplitude of the filter of type 4 with those of filters 2 and 3 in Fig. 4.5. Regarding bouncing, they are slightly accentuated with regard to the filter of type 4. Therefore, we can expect, all other things being equal, poorer stability.

Regarding the slope we see, from the cut-off frequency, a decrease of $-6\,\mathrm{dB}$ per octave for filters of type 2 and type 3 and of $-12\,\mathrm{dB}$ per octave for filter of type 4. This last result is due to an extra pole pertaining to the filter.

The time constant associated with that pole is the only difference between

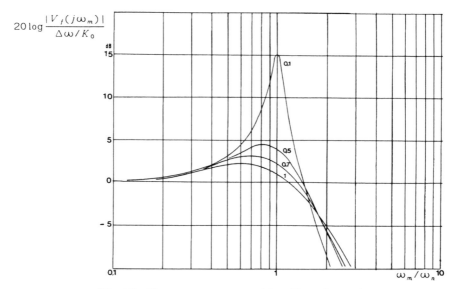

Fig. 4.7   Frequency response with a filter of type 4.

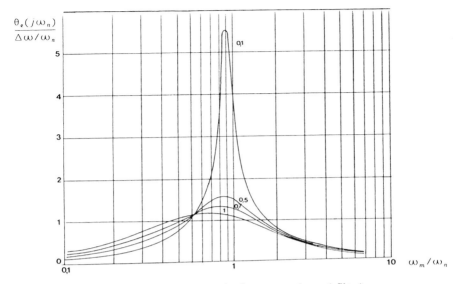

Fig. 4.8 Steady-state peak phase error (type 4 filter).

filters of type 3 and 4. We saw in Chapter 2 that, when this time constant is very small compared with the other two time constants of the loop in which it is involved, the system is quite close to a second-order system.

(b) Steady-state peak phase error

$1 - T(j\omega_m)$ can be deduced from equation (4.25):

$$1 - T(j\omega_m) = \frac{-\omega_m^2[j\omega_m + \omega_n(1 + 2\zeta)]}{(j\omega_m + \omega_n)(-\omega_m^2 + 2\zeta\omega_n j\omega_m + \omega_n^2)} \tag{4.27}$$

Then setting $x = \omega_m/\omega_n$ and calculating the magnitude of expression (4.27), we obtain

$$|1 - T(j\omega_m)| = \frac{x^2[x^2 + (1 + 2\zeta)^2]^{1/2}}{(1 + x^2)^{1/2}[(1 - x^2)^2 + 4\zeta^2 x^2]^{1/2}} \tag{4.28}$$

This last equation combined with equation (4.10) shows that

$$\frac{|\Theta_e(j\omega_m)|}{\Delta\omega/\omega_n} = \left|\frac{1 - T(j\omega_m)}{\omega_m/\omega_n}\right| = \frac{x[x^2 + (1 + 2\zeta)^2]^{1/2}}{(1 + x^2)^{1/2}[(1 - x^2)^2 + 4\zeta^2 x^2]^{1/2}} \tag{4.29}$$

Equation (4.29) is plotted in Fig. 4.8 for different values of the damping factor.

The preceding results for the third-order loop were obtained supposing that $\zeta \leqslant 1$.

5

Operating ranges

In Chapter 4, we dealt with tracking. Since the PLL was locked, we used a linear model. In this chapter, we shall be confronted with three main items: lock limits, capture and unlocking. Lock limits define the hold range, capture is related to the lock-in and pull-in ranges and unlocking to the pull-out range. Regarding the hold range the linear model can still be used. However, as far as the other ranges are concerned, the linear assumption is discarded.

5.1 HOLD RANGE

5.1.1 First-order loop

Since in this case there is no filter, results found in section 1.2.4 will still apply.
We saw that the hold range was as follows

$$|\Delta\omega_H| = \omega_n = K_v$$

This result is quite coherent since the angular frequency ω_n corresponds to the $-3\,dB$ bandwidth.

5.1.2 Loops with a filter

The maximum voltage value which drives the oscillator is reached when $\theta_e = \pi/2$.
The step $\Delta\omega_H$ has the following Laplace transform:

$$\Omega(s) = \frac{\Delta\omega_H}{s}$$

Thus

$$\Theta(s) = \frac{\Delta\omega_H}{s^2}$$

In Chapter 3, we calculated the phase error $\theta_e(\infty)$ corresponding to an angular frequency step for every type of filter. We found the following results. For passive filters (types 1 and 2),

$$[\theta_e(t)]_{t \to \infty} = \frac{\Delta\omega_H}{K_v}$$

and for active filters (types 3 and 4),

$$[\theta_e(t)]_{t \to \infty} = \frac{\Delta\omega_H}{AK_v}$$

If we do not take into account the approximation $\sin \theta_e(t) \approx \theta_e(t)$, we then have

$$\lim [\sin \theta_e(\infty)] = \frac{|\Delta\omega_H|}{K_v}$$

Since 1 is the maximum limit of $\sin \theta_e(t)$, we shall have the hold range

$$|\Delta\omega_H| = K_v$$

for the passive filters and

$$|\Delta\omega_H| = AK_v$$

for the active filters.

Since the operational amplifier gain A is considered as infinite, the hold range will also be infinite. Therefore, in this case, the tuning range of the oscillator will be the limit.

5.2 CAPTURE PROCESS

Normally the loop will remain in lock throughout the hold range. However, if is unlocked it may not be able to acquire lock even if the frequency is close to the frequency limits of the hold range. Actually, that is what happens and this accounts for why the hold range is greater than the capture range.

5.2.1 Lock-in (quick capture)

In order to be able to apply the rotating vector diagram, we shall represent it with a reference vector whose rotating angular frequency is equal to the free-running frequency of the VCO ω_0. Therefore, the point H is at noon and the voltage v_f is zero (Fig. 5.1).

Let us increase, at time $t = 0$, the angular frequency of the reference signal from ω_0 to ω_r. We then have

$$\omega_r - \omega_0 = \Delta\omega(0) = \Delta\omega_L$$
$$\omega_r - \omega_L(t) = \Delta\omega(t)$$

where $\Delta\omega(0) = \Delta\omega_L$ is the maximum lock-in range.

Once the capture has been achieved, the extremity of the vector $\overrightarrow{OH}$ will reach

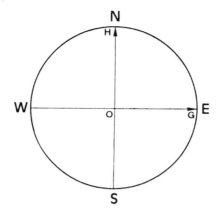

Fig. 5.1   Vector diagram illustrating two signals applied to the PC. Their common frequency is equal to the VCO free-running frequency.

its equilibrium position, denoted H_L. It corresponds to the angular frequency ω_r.

Let us now consider a vector $\overrightarrow{OM}$, rotating with an angular frequency equal to $\Delta\omega(t)$, whose magnitude is $K_d|F[j\,\Delta\omega(t)]|$ and whose projection along the WE axis represents the voltage applied to the VCO. That is to say,

$$v_f = K_d \cos(\Delta\omega\, t + \phi)|F[j\,\Delta\omega(t)]|$$

In order to reach the point H_L, a voltage equal to the projection of $\overrightarrow{OH_L}$ along the WE axis must be applied to the VCO. To fulfil this condition, we must have

$$|\overrightarrow{OM}| = K_d|F[j\,\Delta\omega(0)]| \geqslant \text{proj } \overrightarrow{OH_L}$$

In that case we may expect that the capture will be rapid, because, to reach

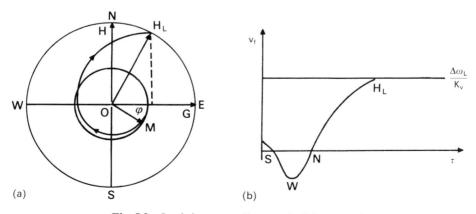

Fig. 5.2   Lock-in vector diagram (quick capture).

the equilibrium point H_L, it is not necessary for the vector $\overrightarrow{OM}$ to make several turns. In Fig. 5.2(a) we have represented the vector $\overrightarrow{OM}$ in its initial and final positions. The initial position depends on the error phase between the reference and the VCO signals at time $t = 0$. In the final position M has reaches H_L. During the lock-in the point M will follow up a trajectory close to that indicated in Fig. 5.2.

We have represented in Fig. 5.2(b) v_f as function of time. We can see that the lock takes place within one single beat between reference frequency and VCO frequency.

The lock-in condition is given below:

$$\Delta\omega_L \leqslant K_v |F(j\,\Delta\omega_L)|$$

Let us next evaluate $K_v |F(j\,\Delta\omega_L)|$, assuming that $\Delta\omega_L$ is large enough, so that the following approximations regarding the transfer functions, can be used for the filters of types 1, 2, 3, and 4:

type 1
$$\frac{1}{\tau\,\Delta\omega_L}$$

type 2
$$\frac{\tau_2}{\tau + \tau_2}$$

type 3
$$\frac{\tau_2}{\tau_1}$$

type 4
$$\frac{\tau_2}{\tau_1(1 + \Delta\omega_L^2\,\tau_3^2)^{1/2}}$$

For the filter of type 1, we obtain

$$\frac{K_v}{\tau\,\Delta\omega_L} = \Delta\omega_L$$

from which we find that

$$\Delta\omega_L = \left(\frac{K_v}{\tau}\right)^{1/2} = \omega_n$$

We deduce, from this result, that a reference signal whose angular frequency is $\omega_0 + \Delta\omega_L$ will lock, probably quickly, if the difference of its angular frequency with respect to that of the VCO is equal to the natural angular frequency of the system.

With a filter of type 2, we obtain

$$\Delta\omega_L = K_v \frac{\tau_2}{\tau_1 + \tau_2} = \tau_2\omega_n^2 = \frac{\omega_n^2}{K_v}\left(\frac{2\zeta K_v}{\omega_n} - 1\right)$$

which can be simplified when

$$K_v \gg \omega_n$$

and we then find

$$\Delta\omega_L = 2\zeta\omega_n$$

From a filter of type 3, we have

$$\Delta\omega_L = K_v \frac{\tau_2}{\tau_1} = 2\zeta\omega_n$$

Finally, let us evaluate the lock-in range of a type 4 filter from the following equation:

$$\Delta\omega_L = \frac{\tau_2 K_v}{\tau_1(1 + \Delta\omega_L^2 \tau_3^2)^{1/2}} \qquad (5.1)$$

Setting $\Delta\omega_L = x$, squaring both sides of equation (5.1) and acquiring a common denominator, we obtain

$$x^4 + \frac{x^2}{\tau_3^2} - \left(\frac{\tau_2}{\tau_1\tau_3}\right)^2 K_v^2 = 0$$

and thus

$$x = \frac{\sqrt{2}}{2}\frac{1}{\tau_3}\left\{-1 + \left[1 + 4\left(\frac{\tau_2\tau_3}{\tau_1}K_v\right)^2\right]^{1/2}\right\}^{1/2} \qquad (5.2)$$

Equations (2.81) and (2.85), those corresponding to the case where the semi-straight lines from the origin of the p plane are tangential to the root locus, allow us to re-write equation (5.2) as follows:

$$\Delta\omega_L = \frac{\sqrt{2}}{2}\omega_n(1 + 2\zeta)\left\{-1 + \left[1 + \frac{4}{(1 + 2\zeta)^2}\right]^{1/2}\right\}^{1/2}$$

The limits of ζ being $\sqrt{2}/2$ and 1, we find respectively

$$\Delta\omega_L = 0.93\,\omega_n$$
$$\Delta\omega_L = 0.95\,\omega_n$$

Practically, in this particular case, the lock-in is the same as for the filter of type 1.

Remark. The lock-in process is not instantaneous. According to Best [2], its duration is approximately given by

$$T_l \approx \frac{1}{\omega_n} \qquad (5.3)$$

for any filter.

5.2.2 Pull-in (slow capture)

Let us increase, at time $t = 0$, the reference angular frequency from ω_0 to ω_r:

$$\omega_r - \omega_0 = \Delta\omega(0) = \Delta\omega_P$$
$$\omega_r - \omega_L(t) = \Delta\omega(t)$$

Then the voltage at the filter output, at time $t = 0$, is

$$v_f = K_d |F(j\,\Delta\omega_P)|\cos\phi$$

In the vector diagram the equilibrium point, corresponding to a reference angular frequency equal to $\omega_0 + \Delta\omega_P$, is denoted by H_P (Fig. 5.3(a)).

As in the previous case, we shall use the vector $\overrightarrow{OM}$ whose projection along the WE axis represents the voltage applied to the VCO input. In this case, as can be seen in Fig. 5.3(a), the projection of $\overrightarrow{OM}$ is not large enough to synchronize the VCO with the incoming signal, since we have

$$K_v |F(j\,\Delta\omega_P)| < \Delta\omega_p$$

Therefore, $\overrightarrow{OM}$ will rotate clockwise, if $\Delta\omega_P > 0$, with speed equal to $\Delta\omega(t)$. Since along the points W, N and E the projection of $\overrightarrow{OM}$ increases it will reduce the speed $\Delta\omega(t)$. Thus, it will modulate the VCO in the positive direction (towards ω_r). On the contrary, along the points E, S and W $\Delta\omega(t)$ will incerease and the VCO will be modulated in the negative direction. Therefore, it will result that the semiperiods corresponding to a positive modulation will be longer than those corresponding to a negative modulation (Fig. 5.3(b)). Owing to this asymmetry, the average voltage at the filter output is not null and slightly positive and thus it pulls the VCO frequency towards the reference frequency. At the same time, the filter will attenuate less and the magnitude of $\overrightarrow{OM}$ will increase (Fig. 5.4).

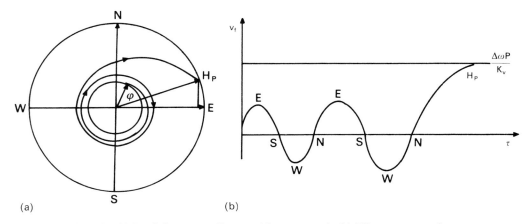

Fig. 5.3 (a) Lock-in vector diagram (slow capture). (b) Filter output voltage.

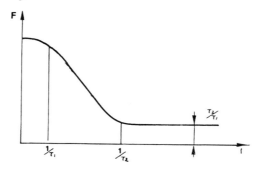

Fig. 5.4   Transfer curve of a type 3 filter.

Both effects cause a regenerative process. The point M will describe a kind of spiral and, eventually, it will reach the point H_P, its target, where it will remain motionless.

We have represented in Fig. 5.3(b) v_f as function of time.

Each time the point M does a complete turn, it corresponds to a cycle whose period increases with time. Therefore, the necessary time for the system to reach the equilibrium point H_P will depend on the number of turns and on the speed with which they are taken. One can imagine that it can be rather long, depending on the time constants of the filter (Fig. 5.5).

The pull-in can be very long, and therefore it is worthwhile having an idea of its duration T_P. Several authors have proposed some formulas based on approximations. We shall retain the results obtained by Best [2] related to filters of types 2 and 3. As far as the filter of type 2 is concerned, we have assumed, in

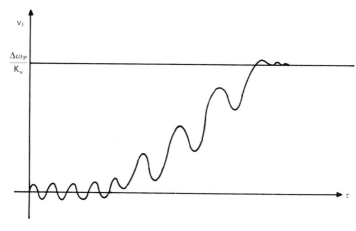

Fig. 5.5   Output filter voltage (slow capture).

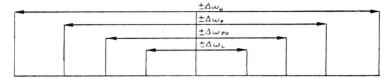

Fig. 5.6 Operating range diagram.

order to simplify, that $K_v \gg \omega_n$.

$$\Delta\omega_P \approx \frac{8}{\pi}(\zeta\omega_n K_v)^{1/2} \qquad (5.4)$$

$$T_P = \frac{\Delta\omega_P^2}{2\zeta\omega_n^3} \qquad (5.5)$$

5.3 PULL-OUT RANGE

Tracking may be lost in this range as a result, for instance, of a frequency impulse. Normally, however, the PLL will lock again. Depending on the amplitude of the impulse, the return to synchronization can be very slow, specially if it is a pull-in process.

The pull-out range is given by a formula determined from computer simulations. For a second-order loop, the following formula has been proposed:

$$\Delta\omega_{PO} = 1.8\omega_n(\zeta + 1) \qquad (5.6)$$

5.4 OPERATING RANGE SPECTRUM

Figure 5.6 shows the ranges in which PLLs operate. Static and dynamic limits of stability are indicated in the figure. It is worth noting that

$$\Delta\omega_L < \Delta\omega_{PO} < \Delta\omega_P < \Delta\omega_H$$

6

Noise

In the preceding chapter, we determined the operating ranges of the PLL, without referring to the noise, which will be treated now. We shall see, in particular, the noise problems regarding the acquisition and how to solve them.

In order to avoid significant mathematical development related to statistics, a certain number of results will be given without proof. On the contrary, results based on operational calculus will either be treated or be given in the appendix.

6.1 NOISE AT THE INPUT LOOP

Let $e(t)$ be a random signal whose spectrum is given in Fig. 6.1. Its power spectral density is N_0. Its bandwidth, theoretically infinite, is limited by a filter whose bandwidth is from $f - B_i/2$ to $f + B_i/2$.

When a signal such as $e(t)$ is present together with a sinusoidal signal at the input of an analogue multiplier it can be shown that [6]

$$E_r \cos(\omega_t t + \phi_r) + e(t) \equiv E_r \cos[\omega_r t + \phi_r + \theta_{nr}(t)]$$

Everything then happens as if the reference signal were a sinusoidal signal whose phase was modulated by the noise. Such a noise will cause a random displacement of the zero-crossing points of the sinusoidal signal. It can be shown that

$$\overline{\theta_{nr}^2(t)} = \frac{2N_0 \times B_i/2}{E_r^2} \tag{6.1}$$

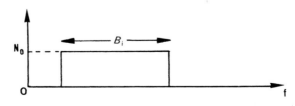

Fig. 6.1 Noise spectrum.

where $N_0 B_i$ is the power P_{nr} corresponding to the noise measured at the terminals of a $1\,\Omega$ resistor. Thus

$$P_{nr} = N_0 B_i$$

$2N_0/E_r^2$ is the unilateral spectral power density. It is expressed in square radians per hertz.

The power P_{sr} associated with the reference signal is $E_r^2/2$, when measured at the terminals of a $1\,\Omega$ resistor.

We then have

$$\overline{\theta_{nr}^2(t)} = \frac{P_{nr}}{2 P_{sr}}$$

Let $|\mathrm{SNR}|_r$ be the signal noise ratio P_{sr}/P_{nr}. We obtain

$$\overline{\theta_{nr}^2(t)} = \frac{1}{2|\mathrm{SNR}|_r} \tag{6.2}$$

6.2   LOOP NOISE

The noise process being random and Gaussian, the mean value $\overline{\theta(t)}$ is null. Thus, we shall evaluate $\overline{\theta^2(t)}$ using Parseval's theorem.

$$\int_{-\infty}^{\infty} \theta^2(t)\,\mathrm{d}t = \frac{1}{2\pi} \int_{-\infty}^{\infty} \Theta(-\mathrm{j}\omega)\,\Theta(\mathrm{j}\omega)\,\mathrm{d}\omega$$
$$= \int_{-\infty}^{\infty} |\Theta(\mathrm{j}\omega)|^2\,\mathrm{d}f$$

where $\Theta(\mathrm{j}\omega)$ is the Fourier transform of $\theta(t)$.

We have to calculate the mean square $\overline{\theta^2(t)}$ over a time T_0 long enough for the variable $\theta(t)$ to be well represented. We assume that its value is null outside the interval $[-T_0/2, +T_0/2]$.

We then have

$$\int_{-\infty}^{\infty} \theta^2(t)\,\mathrm{d}t = \int_{-T_0/2}^{T_0/2} \theta^2(t)\,\mathrm{d}t$$

and according to Parseval's theorem

$$\int_{-T_0/2}^{T_0/2} \theta^2(t)\,\mathrm{d}t = \int_{-\infty}^{\infty} |\Theta(\mathrm{j}\omega)|^2\,\mathrm{d}f$$

Dividing both sides of the preceding equation by T_0, we obtain

$$\frac{1}{T_0} \int_{-T_0/2}^{T_0/2} \theta^2(t)\,\mathrm{d}t = \int_{-\infty}^{\infty} \frac{|\Theta(\mathrm{j}\omega)|^2}{T_0}\,\mathrm{d}f$$

Next, let T_0 approach infinity in order to provide a good characterization of $\theta(t)$. Eventually, we have

$$\overline{\theta^2(t)} = \lim_{T_0 \to \infty} \left[\frac{1}{T_0} \int_{-T_0/2}^{T_0/2} \theta^2(t)\, dt \right] = \int_{-\infty}^{\infty} \frac{2|\Theta(j\omega)|^2}{T_0}\, df \qquad (6.3)$$

The expression $2|\Theta(j\omega)|^2/T_0$ is the unilateral power spectral density. It is expressed in radians squared per hertz.

Let $\theta_{nr}(t)$ be a noise signal applied to the input of a linear system whose transfer function is $T(j\omega)$ and whose unit-impulse response is $h(t)$.

Let $\Theta_{nr}(j\omega)$ and noise $\Theta_{nl}(j\omega)$ respectively be the Fourier transforms of the input and output signals. According to Duhamel's theorem, we have

$$\Theta_{nl}(j\omega) = |T(j\omega)|\Theta_{nr}(j\omega)$$

Squaring both sides of the preceding equation, we find

$$\Theta_{nl}^2(j\omega) = |T(j\omega)|^2 \Theta_{nr}^2(j\omega) \qquad (6.4)$$

From equations (6.3) and (6.4), we find

$$\overline{\theta_{nl}^2(t)} = \int_{-\infty}^{\infty} \frac{2\Theta_{nl}^2(j\omega)}{T_0}\, df = \int_{0}^{\infty} \frac{2\Theta_{nr}^2(j\omega)}{T_0}|T(j\omega)|^2\, df \qquad (6.5)$$

Next, from equation (6.1), the unilateral power spectral density is $2N_0/E_r^2$, and thus

$$\frac{N_0}{E_r^2} = \frac{\Theta_{nr}^2(j\omega)}{T_0}$$

and

$$\overline{\theta_{nl}^2(t)} = \frac{2N_0}{E_r^2} \int_{0}^{\infty} |T(j\omega)|^2\, df \qquad (6.6)$$

This last equation, taking into account equation (6.1), can be re-written as follows

$$\overline{\theta_{nl}^2(t)} = \frac{2\overline{\theta_{nr}^2(t)}}{B_i} \int_{0}^{\infty} |T(j\omega)|^2\, df \qquad (6.7)$$

The expression

$$B_n = \int_{0}^{\infty} |T(j\omega)|^2\, df \qquad (6.8)$$

is called the unilateral equivalent noise bandwidth and, combining it with equation (6.7), it can be re-written as

$$\overline{\theta_{nl}^2(t)} = 2\overline{\theta_{nr}^2(t)}\frac{B_n}{B_i} \qquad (6.9)$$

Let us put, by analogy with equation (6.2),

$$\overline{\theta_{nl}^2(t)} = \frac{1}{2|SNR|_l} \tag{6.10}$$

From equations (6.2), (6.9) and (6.10), we find

$$|SNR| = \frac{B_i}{2B_n}|SNR|_r \tag{6.11}$$

We see that the signal to noise ratio in the loop is proportional to the inverse of B_n.

6.3   NOISE-EQUIVALENT BANDWIDTH ACCORDING TO THE DIFFERENT FILTERS

6.3.1   Loop without a filter ($|F(j\omega)| = 1$)

The closed-loop transfer function is, according to equation (2.17), where we have replaced s with $j\omega$ and set $|F(j\omega)| = 1$,

$$T(j\omega) = \frac{K_v}{j\omega + K_v}$$

Thus

$$B_n = \frac{1}{2\pi} \int_0^\infty \frac{K_v^2}{K_v^2 + \omega^2} \, d\omega = \frac{K_v}{4}$$

If we express K_v in radians per second, B_n is expressed in hertz.

Since K_v must be very large for stability reasons, B_n will also be large. Therefore, without a filter, as expected the protection against noise is very poor.

6.3.2   Loop with a filter of type 1

The loop transfer function is given by equation (2.21) from which we deduce

$$T(j\omega) = \frac{\omega_n^2}{\omega_n^2 - \omega^2 + 2j\zeta\omega_n\omega}$$

Squaring both sides of this last equation, we obtain

$$|T(j\omega)|^2 = \frac{\omega_n^4}{(\omega_n^2 - \omega^2)^2 + 4\zeta^2\omega_n^2\omega^2}$$

Substituting it into equation (6.8), after having set $x = \omega/\omega_n$, gives the following equation:

$$B_n = \frac{\omega_n}{2\pi} \int_0^\infty \frac{dx}{(1 - x^2)^2 + 4\zeta x^2} \tag{6.12}$$

Integration produces the result

$$B_n = \frac{\omega_n}{8\zeta} \tag{6.13}$$

This can be re-written, using relations (2.20), as follows:

$$B_n = \frac{K_v}{4}$$

It is an amazing result, as it is the same as that found with the loop without filter. As far as noise is concerned, this loop is not better.

6.3.3   Loop with a filter of type 2

Following the same method as in the preceding section, from equation (2.32) we obtain

$$B_n = \frac{\omega_n}{2\pi} \int_0^\infty \frac{1 + (2\zeta - \omega_n/K_v)^2 x^2}{(1 - x^2)^2 + 4\zeta^2 x^2} \, dx \tag{6.14}$$

This type of integral is found in many books. The result is

$$B_n = \frac{\omega_n}{8\zeta} \left[1 + \left(2\zeta - \frac{\omega_n}{K_v} \right)^2 \right] \tag{6.15}$$

6.3.4   Loop with a filter of type 3

Equation (2.50) was obtained from equation (2.32), setting ω_n/K_v equal to 0. Notice that these equations represent the closed-loop transfer functions corresponding to filters of types 2 and 3.

   Therefore, if we do the same in equation (6.15), we obtain the noise-equivalent bandwidth of the filter of type 3:

$$B_n = \frac{\omega_n}{8\zeta} (1 + 4\zeta^2) \tag{6.16}$$

   In Fig. 6.2, B_n/ω_n is plotted against ζ. This figure shows that B_n is at a minimum when ζ is equal to 1/2 and since the curve is rather flat around this point it justifies the choice of $\sqrt{2}/2$ for the damping factor.

6.3.5   Loop with a filter of type 4

The closed-loop transfer function loop for this type of filter is given by equation (2.59).

   We shall determine the noise-equivalent bandwidth B_n corresponding to the case where the semistraight lines from the origin of the p plane are tangential

Since we are interested in the d.c. component, that is to say the mean value, we shall evaluate it. It is a very important value because it is applied at the input of the VCO whose frequency will track the reference frequency.

In the case represented in Fig. 7.3, we have

$$\frac{\bar{V}_s}{R_C I_{EE}/2v_T} = V_m \left(-\frac{1}{\pi} \int_0^\phi \sin u \, du + \frac{1}{\pi} \int_\phi^\pi \sin u \, du \right)$$

$$= \frac{V_m}{\pi} [\cos u]_0^\phi - \frac{V_m}{\pi} [\cos u]_\phi^\pi$$

$$= \frac{V_m}{\pi} (\cos \phi - 1) - \frac{V_m}{\pi} (\cos\pi - \cos \phi)$$

$$= \frac{2V_m}{\pi} \cos \phi$$

Therefore

$$\bar{V}_s = \frac{R_C I_{EE} V_m}{\pi v_T} \cos \phi \qquad (7.18)$$

As we did in Chapter 1, let us set

$$\phi = \frac{\pi}{2} - \theta_e$$

Therefore, when $\theta_e = 0$, $\bar{V}_s = 0$ and the frequency of the reference signal is equal to the free-running frequency of the VCO.

We then obtain

$$\bar{V}_s = \frac{R_C I_{EE} V_m}{\pi v_T} \sin \theta_e \qquad (7.19)$$

From the preceding equation, it can be seen that the PC is of the sinusoidal type, in spite of the fact that one of the signals is of the square-wave type.

It is worth noting the dependence of the comparator gain on the amplitude V_m of the signal.

(b)   Triangular characteristic

Two cases are considred here.

In the first case, both input signals have a large amplitude: $v_{i1}, v_{i2} \gg 2v_T$. This case occurs when the reference input of the comparator is a limiter that produces a near-constant amplitude for FM purposes. Figure 7.4 represents two square-wave signals and their product obtained by means of the PC.

In the second case, both signals v_{i1} and v_{i2} have the same frequency and they are out of phase by ϕ. Let us evaluate the d.c. component following the multiplica-

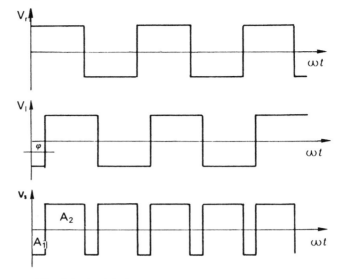

Fig. 7.4   Multiplication of two square-wave signals.

tion of the two input signals. Over a period π/ω, we have (Fig. 7.4)

$$\bar{V}_S = \frac{1}{\pi}(A_2 - A_1)$$

$$= R_C I_{EE} \frac{1}{\pi}(\pi - \phi - \phi) \qquad (7.20)$$

$$= R_C I_{EE}\left(1 - \frac{2\phi}{\pi}\right)$$

We plot the function $\bar{V}_S = f(\phi)$ in Fig. 7.5. As can be seen, it is of the triangular type.

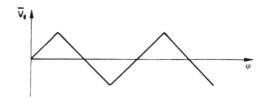

Fig. 7.5   Comparator characteristic.

(c) Gain

Comparator of the sinusoidal type. Let g_m be the transconductance of transistors Q_1 and Q_2 (Fig. 7.1).

We have

$$\frac{1}{g_m} = \frac{v_T}{I_{EE}/2}$$

and inserting this into equation (7.19) gives

$$\bar{V}_S = \frac{2}{\pi} g_m R_C V_m \sin \theta_e \qquad (7.21)$$

Setting $A_d = g_m R_C$, equation (7.21) is re-written:

$$\bar{V}_S = \frac{2}{\pi} A_d V_m \sin \theta_e \qquad (7.22a)$$

Since we have (refer to equation (1.2))

$$v_d = K_d \sin \theta_e$$

$\bar{V}_S = v_d$, we then have

$$K_d = \frac{2}{\pi} A_d V_m \qquad (7.22b)$$

Therefore, the gain depends on the amplitude V_m of the reference signal.

Thus, the hold range will also depend on V_m, according to the following relationship:

$$\Delta \omega_H = \pm K_0 \frac{2}{\pi} A_d V_m \qquad (7.23)$$

This is only valid if

$$V_m < 50\,\text{mV}$$

Otherwise, the input stage of the comparator will saturate.

Comparator of the triangular type. The four-quadrant comparator has a triangular characteristic when the amplitudes of the input signals are large enough to saturate the input stage. The value is fixed around 50 mV.

We set $\phi = \pi/2 - \theta_e$, and equation (7.20) is re-written:

$$\bar{V}_S = \frac{2R_C I_{EE}}{\pi} \theta_e$$

From this we obtain the expression for the gain:

$$K_d = \frac{2}{\pi} R_C I_{EE} \qquad (7.24)$$

Let us evaluate the hold range when filters of types 1 and 2 are used.

$$\bar{V}_S = \frac{2R_C I_{EE}}{\pi} \theta_e = v_d = K_d \theta_e \qquad (7.25)$$

since

$$\Delta\omega = K_0 v_f$$
$$F(0) = 1$$

and

$$v_d = v_f$$

Thus

$$\Delta\omega = K_d K_0 \theta_e$$

and when $\theta_e = \pi/2$, then

$$\Delta\omega_H = K_d K_0 \theta_e = K_v \frac{\pi}{2} \qquad (7.26)$$

An important result shown by equation (7.25) is that a PLL using a four-quadrant comparator has a hold range which can be controlled by means of a current.

(d)   Practical example

We shall study the PC of the integrated circuit 560 (Fig. 7.6), whose output is connected to a d.c. shift level.

Let us evaluate the peak–peak voltage, at the output of the d.c. shift level, when the signals applied at the inputs of the comparator are both of the square-wave type.

Let us assume that the two signals v_{i1} and v_{i2} are simultaneously positive in which case the two transistors Q_1 and Q_4 are on and Q_2, Q_6 and Q_3 are off (Fig. 7.4).

We then have

$$V_A \approx V_{cc}$$
$$V_B \approx V_{cc} - R_C I_{EE}$$

and

$$V_a = (V_{CC} - V_{BE_7} - V_{Z_1}) \frac{R_2}{R_1 + R_2}$$

$$V_b = (V_{CC} - R_C i_{EE} - V_{BE_8} - V_{Z_2}) \frac{R_2}{R_1 + R_2}$$

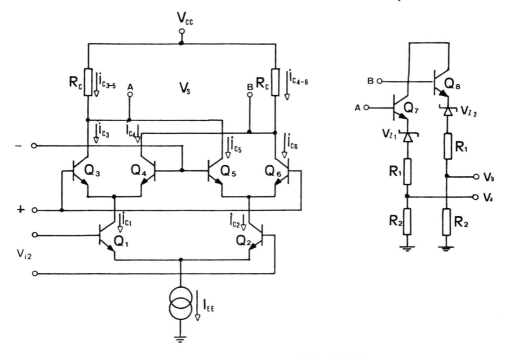

Fig. 7.6 Phase comparator of the 560 IC.

Assuming that $V_{BE_7} = V_{BE_8}$ and $V_{Z_1} = V_{Z_2}$, we obtain

$$V_a - V_b = R_C I_{EE} \frac{R_2}{R_1 + R_2}$$

From equation (7.24), we determine the combined gain of the four-quadrant comparator and the d.c. shift level. That is to say,

$$K_d = \frac{2}{\pi} R_C I_{EE} \frac{R_2}{R_1 + R_2} \tag{7.27}$$

Taking into account the component values indicated in the circuit diagram, with a current $I_{EE} = 0.75\,\text{mA}$, we find

$$K_d = \frac{2}{\pi} \times 6 \times 0.75 \times \frac{8.2}{8.2 + 1.2} \text{V rad}^{-1} = 2.5\,\text{V rad}^{-1}$$

In the case of a sinusoidal characteristic, we calculate the gain from equation (7.22b) replacing A_d with

$$\frac{R_C I_{EE}}{v_T\,2}$$

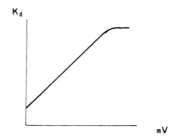

Fig. 7.7   Gain of the comparator: K_d.

We obtain

$$K_d = \frac{2}{\pi} R_C I_{EE} \frac{V_m}{v_T} \frac{R_1}{R_1 + R_2} \qquad (7.28)$$

Since $v_T \approx 26\,\text{mV}$,

$$K_d(\text{mV rad}^{-1}) = 6000 \times \frac{0.75}{26\pi} \times \frac{8.2}{8.2 + 1.2} = 48\,V_m$$

The formula is valid for $V_m \leqslant 50\,\text{mV}$. The plot of $K_d = f(V_m)$ is illustrated in Fig. 7.7.

Care must be taken regarding the reference amplitude value which is applied to the phase comparator because it changes its gain.

Since the gain K_d is a function of the bias current I_{EE} it can be adjusted by the user. In the application notes the plots of $K_d = f(\phi, I_{EE})$ are given (Fig. 7.8).

We saw that the hold range depended on the reference voltage amplitude V_m,

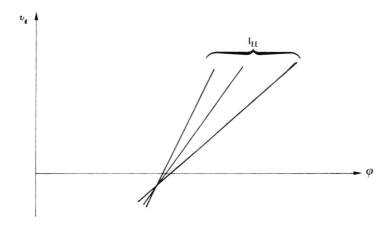

Fig. 7.8   Comparator output voltage versus phase error and bias current.

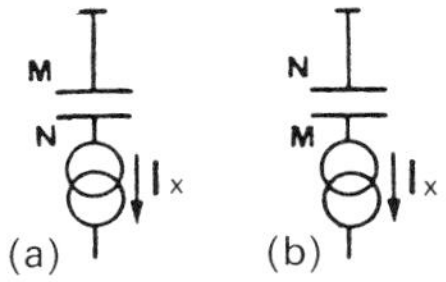

Fig. 7.13 Capacitor charging.

and since

$$V_{D_2} = V_{BE_4} = V_{BE_1} = V_{BE}$$

we find

$$V_N = V_{CC} - 3V_{BE}$$

transistor Q_1 turns on and the potential between the two terminals of the capacitor is then V_{BE}.

As soon as transistor Q_1 turns on, diode D_1 turns on too, and the base potential of transistor Q_3 as well as its emitter potential $V_{D_1} = V_{BE}$ will decrease, turning off transistor Q_2 and diode D_2. Therefore, the voltage drop in resistor R_2 is negligible, causing a potential increase of V_{BE} on the N plate of the capacitor. Since it cannot discharge instantaneously, the potential on M will go up to $V_{CC} - V_{BE}$. On the other hand, the base potential of transistor Q_2, from the moment Q_1 is on, is $V_{CC} - 2V_{BE}$. This causes the emitter of transistor Q_2 to be reverse biased at a potential equal to V_{BE}.

As far as the capacitor is concerned, it is now in the situation indicated in Fig. 7.13(b). The potential at its terminals is reversed. Thus, the new half-cycle is symmetrical with respect to the preceding one. It ends when M reaches a potential equal to $V_{CC} - 3V_{BE}$. From this very moment, the situation is the same as at time $t = 0$. The potential variation, during a half-cycle, at the capacitor terminals is $2V_{BE}$. Thus, we have

$$2C_x V_{BE} = I_x \frac{T}{2}$$

from which we deduce the frequency

$$f = \frac{I_x}{4C_x V_{BE}}$$

Since the frequency is controlled by a current, the filter output voltage v_f is converted into a current by means of a transconductance amplifier. The complete circuit diagram of the oscillator and the transconductance amplifier is given in Fig. 7.14.

The five current generators in the circuit are identical and deliver the same current I_0. They are represented in Fig. 7.15. Current evaluation gives

$$I_0 = \frac{2V_{BE} - V_{BE}}{R_0} = \frac{0.6}{1200} A = 500 \,\mu A$$

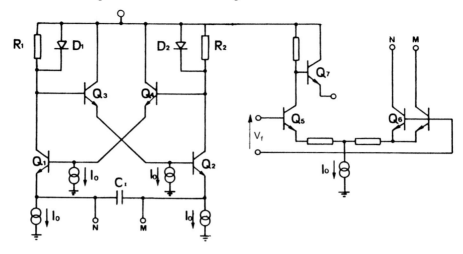

Fig. 7.14   Complete schematic of the VCO.

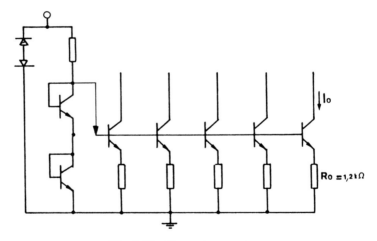

Fig. 7.15   Current generators.

Let us determine the limits of current charging the capacitor C_x. When $v_f = 0$, each branch of the differential amplifier (Fig. 7.14) is supplied with the same current equal to 250 μA. During the charge the capacitor is fed with a current equal to

$$500 + \frac{250}{2}\,\mu A = 625\,\mu A$$

Expressing the capacitance in microfarads, the free-running angular frequency is found to be

$$\omega_0 (\text{rad s}^{-1}) = \frac{\pi I_0}{2C_x V_{BE}} = \frac{\pi}{2} \frac{625}{0.6} \frac{1}{C_x} = \frac{1636}{C_x}$$

When the amplitude v_f is at a maximum and positive the right-hand branch of the differential amplifier (Fig. 7.14) is supplied with a current equal to 500 μA, with no current in the other branch. The current charge of the capacitor C_x will then be 750 μA. The angular frequency of the oscillator then reaches its maximum value:

$$\omega_M (\text{rad s}^{-1}) = \frac{\pi I_0}{2C_x V_{BE}} = \frac{\pi}{2} \frac{750}{0.6} \frac{1}{C_x} = \frac{1963.5}{C_x}$$

Finally, when the amplitude v_f is negative and its magnitude is at a maximum, there is no current supplied to the right-hand branch of the differential amplifier and the capacitor current charge is reduced to 500 μA.

Therefore, the minimum angular frequency is

$$\omega_m (\text{rad s}^{-1}) = \frac{\pi I_0}{2C_x V_{BE}} = \frac{\pi}{2} \frac{500}{0.6} \frac{1}{C_x} = \frac{1309}{C_x}$$

The VCO gain factor K_0 can now be calculated and is found to be

$$K_0 = \frac{d\omega}{dv_f} = \frac{d\omega}{dI_x} \frac{dI_x}{dv_f} \tag{7.31}$$

where I_x, we recall, is the current charging the capacitor C_x.

Since we have

$$\omega = \frac{\pi I_x}{2C_x V_{BE}}$$

then

$$\frac{d\omega}{dI_x} = \frac{\pi}{2C_x V_{BE}} \tag{7.32}$$

Combining equations (7.31) and (7.32) with

$$\omega_0 = \frac{\pi I_0}{2C_x V_{BE}}$$

we find

$$K_0 = \frac{\omega_0}{I_0} \frac{dI_x}{dv_f} \tag{7.33}$$

We then calculate dI_x/dv_f.

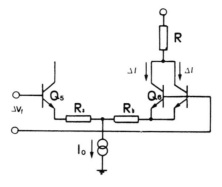

Fig. 7.16   Transconductance amplifier.

Let us connect the right-hand branch of the differential amplifier to a load resistor labelled R_L, as indicated in Fig. 7.16.

Let Δv_L be the voltage at the terminals of resistor R_L; we obtain

$$\frac{\Delta v_L}{\Delta v_f} = \frac{R_L}{2(R_a + r_e)} \tag{7.34}$$

where

$$\frac{1}{g_m} = r_e = \frac{v_T}{I_0/2}$$

and, setting $I_x = I_0 + \Delta I$, we have

$$\frac{dI_x}{dv_f} = \frac{\Delta I}{\Delta v_f}$$

However (Fig. 7.16),

$$\Delta v_L = 2 \Delta I R_L$$

Substituting this relation into equation (7.34), we find

$$\frac{\Delta I}{\Delta v_f} = \frac{1}{4(R_a + r_e)} \tag{7.35}$$

Then, substituting this into equation (7.33), we

$$K_0 = \frac{\omega_0}{I_0} \frac{1}{4(R_a + r_e)} \tag{7.36}$$

and, since $I_0 = 500 \, \mu A$, we obtain

$$r_e = \frac{26}{0.5/2} = 104 \, \Omega$$

and we have $R_a = 325\,\Omega$.

$$K_0(V^{-1}\,rad\,s^{-1}) = 0.9\omega_0 \tag{7.37}$$

K_d being equal to $2.5\,V\,rad^{-1}$, the loop gain is

$$K_v(rad\,s^{-1}) = 2.5 \times 0.9\omega_0 = 2.2\omega_0 \tag{7.38}$$

7.4   BIPOLAR ANALOGUE PLL FAMILY

We present here a series of ICs which is very representative of the linear PLL bipolar family. It is manufactured, among others, by Phillips-Signetics and National Semiconductor.

7.4.1   Circuit 560

Applications include the following:

1. tone decoders;
2. FM IF strips;
3. telemetry decoders;
4. data synchronizers;
5. signal reconstitution;
6. signal generators;
7. modems;
8. tracking filters;
9. subscription carrier authorization (SCA) receivers;
10. frequency shift keying (FSK);
11. wide band high linearity detectors.

7.4.2   Circuit 561

Applications include the following:

1. tone decoders, AM–FM IF strips;
2. telemetry decoders, data synchronizers;
3. signal reconstitution;
4. signal generators;
5. modems;
6. tracking filters;
7. SCA receivers;
8. FSK receivers;
9. wide band high linearity detectors;
10. synchronous detectors;
11. AM receiver.

7.4.3 Circuit 562

Applications include the following:

1. frequency synthesizers;
2. data synchronizers;
3. signal reconstitution;
4. tracking filters;
5. telemetry decoders;
6. modems;
7. FM IF strips and demodulators;
8. tone decoders;
9. FSK receivers;
10. wideband high linearity FM demodulation.

7.4.4 Circuit 564

Applications include the following:

1. high speed modems;
2. FSK receivers and transmitters;
3. frequency synthesizers;
4. signal generators.

7.4.5 Circuit 565

Applications include the following:

1. FSK;
2. modems;
3. telemetry receivers;
4. tone decoders;
5. wideband FM discriminators;
6. data synchronizers;
7. tracking filters;
8. signal restoration;
9. frequency multiplication and division.

7.4.6 Circuit 566

Applications include the following:

1. tone generators;
2. FSK;
3. FM modulators;
4. clock generators;

5. signal generators;
6. function generators.

7.4.7   Circuit 567

Applications include the following:

1. touch-tone decoding;
2. carrier current remote controls;
3. ultrasonic controls (remote TV, etc).;
4. communications paging;
5. frequency monitoring and control;
6. wireless intercom;
7. precision oscillator.

7.4.8   Circuit 568

Applications include the following (operation to 150 MHz):
1. satellite receivers;
2. fibre-optic video links;
3. VHF FSK demodulator;
4. clock recovery.

8

PLLs using digital phase comparators

In the first part of this book, only completely analogue PLLs were studied. In this chapter, we shall study partially digital PLLs, which are becoming very popular. We have separated them from the others because their analysis is different.

They are often called digital PLLs but we think this title is incorrect and can lead to confusion. Strictly speaking this description would require that both error signals and output signals should be digital and this not the case. That is why we prefer to call them semi digital PLL systems.

It can also be justified because it is possible to design and realize PLL systems which are totally digital, namely for certain applications where the analogue loops cannot insure the performances which are required.

As a matter of fact, the PLL semidigital systems are identical to the analogue systems, with the exception of the phase comparator, which is digital. Although there are several types of digital PCs, only two types will be studied: the exclusive-OR comparator and the phase-frequency three-state comparator and charge-pump.

8.1 EXCLUSIVE-OR COMPARATOR

8.1.1 Principle

The circuit is a logic function which implements the operation

$$A\bar{B} + \bar{A}B$$

Applying De Morgan's theorem, it can be written as

$$\overline{\overline{AB} \cdot \overline{A\bar{B}}}$$

whose logic symbol is given in Fig. 8.1.

8.1.2 Comparator characteristic

This type of comparator is very sensitive to the duty cycle ratio of the signals at its inputs. For this reason, we shall study it in two cases: when their duty

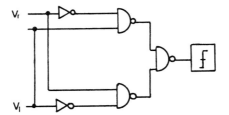

Fig. 8.1 Logic symbol of the comparator.

cycle ratio is 50% and when one of the signals has a duty cycle ratio not equal to 50%.

8.1.3 Input signals

Their duty-cycle ratio is 50%. $v_r(t)$ is the reference signal. $v_l(t)$ is the VCO output signal. ϕ is the phase error.

In Fig. 8.2(a) are illustrated two signals out of phase by $0 < \phi < \pi$. In Fig. 8.2(b) we see two other signals out of phase by $\pi < \phi < 2\pi$. The comparator output signals are also represented in both figures.

When $0 < \phi < \pi$, the average output voltage is

$$\overline{v_d} = V_{DD}\frac{\phi}{\pi}$$

When $\pi < \phi < 2\pi$, the average output voltage is

$$\overline{v_d} = V_{DD}\left(2 - \frac{\phi}{\pi}\right)$$

A plot of the output signal is given in Fig. 8.3. The characteristic is of the triangular type.

8.1.4 One signal has a duty cycle ratio difference of 50%

Figures 8.4(a), 8.4(b) and 8.4(c) correspond to the three following phase errors:

$$0 < \phi + \delta < \pi$$
$$\pi < \phi + \delta < 2\pi \quad \phi > \pi$$
$$\pi < \phi < 2\pi - \delta \quad \phi < \pi$$

The phase wave form diagrams illustrated in Fig. 8.4 allow us to evaluate the average output voltages corresponding to three different cases. We find

$$\overline{v_d} = \frac{V_{DD}}{2}\left(1 - \frac{\delta}{\pi}\right) \tag{8.1}$$

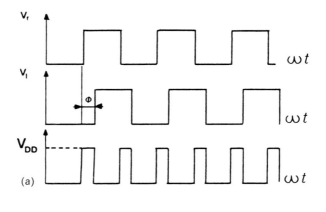

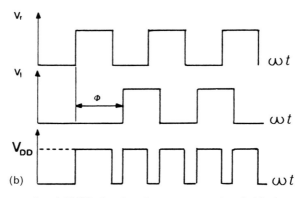

Fig. 8.2   Reference signal, VCO signal and comparator signal: (a) phase error $0 < \phi < \pi$; (b) phase error $\pi < \phi < 2\pi$.

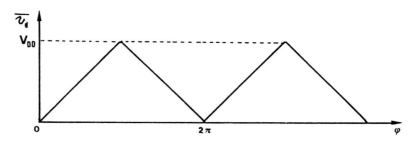

Fig. 8.3   Comparator characteristic.

The third combination, 0 1, leads to the turn-on of the NPN transistor and the cut-off of the PNP transistor. The circuit absorbs a current $-I_p$.

8.2.4 Filters

The charge-pump behaves as a filter whose impedance is $Z_F(s)$. It output voltage is

$$V_F(s) = \pm I_p(s)Z_F(s) \tag{8.2}$$

This voltage is positive when the PNP transistor is turned on and the NPN is cut off, and negative in the reverse case.

8.2.5 Equivalent circuit of the comparator and filter

The device studied so far can be represented by a three-state current switch, as illustrated in Fig. 8.9. The application of Thévenin's theorem allows us to represent the switch as shown in Fig. 8.10.

The use of operational amplifiers together with the filters gives a new series of equivalent circuits illustrated in Figs 8.11 and 8.12.

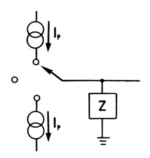

Fig. 8.9 Current switch.

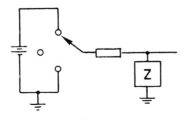

Fig. 8.10 Voltage switch.

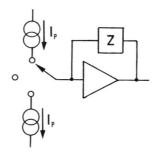

Fig. 8.11   Current switch and operational amplifier.

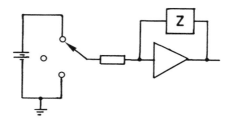

Fig. 8.12   Voltage switch and operational amplifier.

8.2.6   System unlocked

(a)   First case: $\omega_r > \omega_1$

The output corresponds to the output of the complementary stage. With the help of the truth table, we can determine the waveforms and plot them as in Fig. 8.13. When $\bar{H}$ is at its low level, the PNP transistor is on and it delivers the following current to the load:

$$i_d = + I_p \frac{\theta_e}{2\pi}$$

Thus, this current charges the capacitor of the low pass filter when $\bar{H}$ is at its low level. On the contrary, when $\bar{H}$ is at its high level the capacitor is connected to a high impedance allowing the capacitor to retain its charge.

As the current, namely i_d, charges the capacitor, the voltage at its terminals is adjusted until the reference and the VCO signals are equal in both frequency and phase. From this very moment, the filter is permanently connected to a high impedance. At this stable point, both transistors PNP and NPN are off and thus, the phase comparator becomes an open circuit and maintains the voltage of the capacitor of the LPF constant.

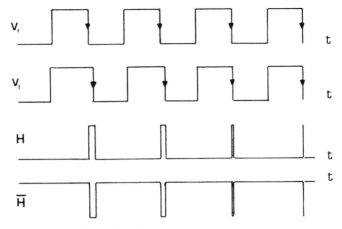

Fig. 8.13   Timing diagram ($\omega_r > \omega_1$).

(b)   Second case: $\omega_r < \omega_1$

The time diagram is illustrated in Fig. 8.14. As can be seen, the NPN transistor is turned on when B is at its high level and it absorbs the following current:

$$i_c = - i_p \frac{\theta_e}{2\pi}$$

It remains cut off for the rest of the time, and is thus connected to a high impedance.

The present situation is the reverse of the preceding case. This time the capacitor discharges until the voltage at its terminal is such that the VCO output and the reference signals become equal in frequency and phase. As in the first case, both transistors PNP and NPN are off. Thus, the phase comparator becomes an open circuit and maintains the voltage of the capacitor of the LPF constant.

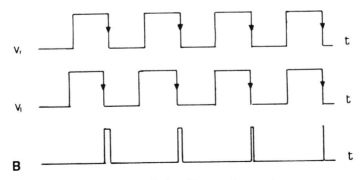

Fig. 8.14   Timing diagram ($\omega_r < \omega_1$).

8.2.7 The system is locked

Since the frequency of the VCO signal and the frequency of the reference signal are equal, we shall study the only two possible cases.

(a) First case: the VCO signal is lagging

Figure 8.15 represents such a case. The PNP transistor is on when $\bar{H} = 0$ and the NPN transistor is maintained cut off all the time since $B = 0$. Therefore, the filter capacitor voltage increases and subsequently the VCO frequency increases, reducing the lag between the two signals, causing this time a reduction of the VCO frequency.

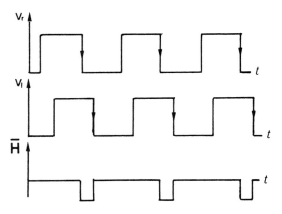

Fig. 8.15 Timing diagram when the VCO signal is lagging.

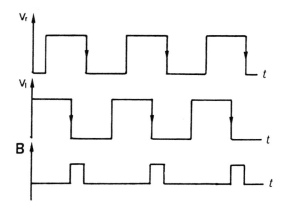

Fig. 8.16 Timing diagram when the reference signal is lagging.

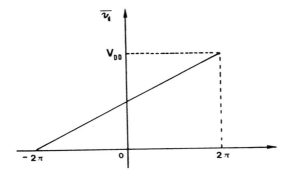

Fig. 8.17 Comparator characteristic.

The cycle proceeds but with a reduced phase error. After a number of cycles, both signals are equal in phase and frequency.

(b) Second case: the reference signal is lagging

This (Fig. 8.16) is exactly the opposite of the preceding case. The PNP transistor is permanently cut-off and the NPN is on when B is at high level.

As in the former case, after a certain number of cycles the two signals are equal in phase and in frequency.

8.2.8 Voltage–frequency transfer curve

The transfer curve of the comparator is illustrated in Fig. 8.17. One can see

1. a phase range from -2π to $+2\pi$, and
2. no periodicity.

8.2.9 Characteristics of the three-state comparator charge-pump

The most remarkable aspects of the performance are

1. sensitivity to both phase and frequency,
2. no phase error between the reference and the VCO signals,
3. no dependence on the duty cycle ratio,
4. digital-to-analogue conversion allowing control of the oscillator.

8.2.10 Closed-loop transfer function

(a) Method of analysis [7]

In principle, the charge-pump PLL is a time-varying network. Therefore, transfer function analysis is not applicable. Nevertheless, if the filter time constant is large

Fig. 8.18　Type 1 filter.

compared with the signal period (or if the loop bandwidth is small compared with the signal frequency), then transfer function theory can be applied.

The charging or discharging current is expressed by the following relationship:

$$V_F = I_p Z_F(s) \frac{\Theta_E(s)}{2\pi} \tag{8.3}$$

However,

$$\Theta_L(s) = \frac{K_0 V_F(s)}{s}$$

and

$$\Theta_E(s) = \Theta_R(s) - \Theta_L(s)$$

Combining the preceding equations, we find

$$\frac{\Theta_L(s)}{\Theta_R(s)} = \frac{K_0 I_p Z_F(s)/2\pi}{s + K_0 I_p Z_F(s)/2\pi} \tag{8.4}$$

$$\frac{\Theta_E(s)}{\Theta_R(s)} = \frac{s}{s + K_0 I_p Z_F(s)/2\pi} \tag{8.5}$$

(b)　Loop with a filter of type 1

The filter is represented in Fig. 8.18. We find its impedance to be

$$Z_F(s) = \frac{1 + \tau s}{s\tau/R} \tag{8.6}$$

Replacing $Z_F(s)$ in equations (8.4) and (8.5) by its value obtained from equation (8.6), we obtain

$$\frac{\Theta_L(s)}{\Theta_R(s)} = \frac{K_0 I_p(R/2\pi)(1 + s\tau)}{\tau s^2 + K_0 I_p(R/2\pi)\tau s + K_0 I_p R/2\pi} \tag{8.7}$$

$$\frac{\Theta_E(s)}{\Theta_R(s)} = \frac{\tau s^2}{\tau s^2 + K_0 I_p(R/2\pi)\tau s + K_0 I_p R/2\pi} \tag{8.8}$$

These equations show that the system is of the second order.

Setting

$$K = K_0 I_p \frac{R}{2\pi}$$

and then dividing both numerator and denominator of equations (8.7) and (8.8) by τ, we obtain

$$\frac{\Theta_L(s)}{\Theta_R(s)} = \frac{K/\tau(1 + s\tau)}{s^2 + Ks + K/\tau} \tag{8.9}$$

$$\frac{\Theta_E(s)}{\Theta_R(s)} = \frac{s^2}{s^2 + Ks + K/\tau} \tag{8.10}$$

Setting

$$K = 2\zeta\omega_n$$

$$\frac{K}{\tau} = \omega_n^2$$

equations (8.9) and (8.10) become

$$\frac{\Theta_L(s)}{\Theta_R(s)} = \frac{\omega_n^2 + 2\zeta\omega_n s}{s^2 + 2\zeta\omega_n s + \omega_n^2} \tag{8.11}$$

$$\frac{\Theta_E(s)}{\Theta_R(s)} = \frac{s^2}{s^2 + 2\zeta\omega_n s + \omega_n^2} \tag{8.12}$$

and we see that the first equation has the same form as equation (2.50).

If we normalize equation (3.27) using equations (2.49), we find that it also has the same form as the second equation. Therefore, all the results related to stability and accuracy (or linear tracking) for a filter of type 3 are also valid for the charge-pump using a filter of type 1.

Regarding stability and tracking, the same performances can be achieved using a simple filter of type 1 instead of a filter of type 3 as is the case with an analogue PC.

Let us recall some particular results when comparing the use of filter 3 in place of filter 1, as far as tracking is concerned:

1. the phase error is zero, instead of $\Delta\omega/K$, when an angular frequency step is applied;
2. the phase error is equal to $(\tau_1/K)\Delta\dot{\omega}$, instead of infinite, when an angular frequency ramp is applied.

The equivalence between a three-state comparator, charge-pump and a filter of type 1 with an analogue comparator and a filter of type 3 can be realized in a more precise way.

When we studied a loop with a filter of type 3, we set

$$\frac{\tau_2}{\tau_1} K_v = 2\zeta\omega_n$$

$$\frac{K_v}{\tau_1} = \omega_n^2$$

Identifying, respectively, these two relationships with

$$K = 2\zeta\omega_n$$

$$\frac{K}{\tau} = \omega_n^2$$

we obtain

$$\tau_1 = \frac{K_v}{K}\tau$$

$$\tau_2 = \tau$$

Therefore, the equivalence between the filters is

$$\frac{1 + s\tau_2}{s\tau_1} \Leftrightarrow \frac{1 + s\tau}{s(K_v/K)\tau}$$

Let us replace in the right-hand side expression K_v and K by $K_d K_0$ and $K_0 I_p R/2\pi$ respectively. This expression then has the following form:

$$\frac{I_p R}{2\pi K_d} \frac{1 + s\tau}{s\tau}$$

Therefore, everything happens as if we had a comparator whose gain factor K_d were $I_p R/2\pi$ and whose associated filter would have the following transfer

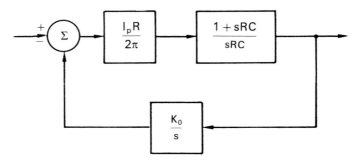

Fig. 8.19   PLL with three-state phase comparator, charge-pump and type 1 filter.

Fig. 8.20   Improved filter.

function:

$$F(s) = \frac{1 + sRC}{sRC}$$

Figure 8.19 represents the equivalent block diagram of a PLL network with a three-state charge-pump comparator and an RC filter (type 3).

(c)   Loop with an improved filter

The simple RC filter can be improved with the association in parallel of a second filter C_1, as shown in Fig. 8.20.

Let us evaluate the impedance $Z_F(s)$ of this filter. We have

$$\frac{1}{Z_F(s)} = sC_1 + \frac{sC}{1 + s\tau}$$

where

$$Z_F(s) = \frac{a - 1}{a} \frac{1 + s\tau}{sC(1 + s\tau/a)} \tag{8.13}$$

and

$$1 + \frac{C}{C_1} = a$$

Replacing $Z_F(s)$ by its value obtained from equation (8.13) in equations (8.4) and (8.5) and setting once again

$$K = \frac{K_0 I_p R}{2\pi}$$

we then find

$$\frac{\Theta_L(s)}{\Theta_R(s)} = K \frac{a - 1}{\tau} \frac{1/\tau + s}{s^3 + (a/\tau)s^2 + K[(a - 1)/\tau]s + K[(a - 1)/\tau^2]} \tag{8.14}$$

and

$$\frac{\Theta_E(s)}{\Theta_R(s)} = \frac{a}{\tau} \frac{s^2(1 + s\tau/a)}{s^3 + (a/\tau)s^2 + K[(a - 1)/\tau]s + K[(a - 1)/\tau^2]} \tag{8.15}$$

The denominator of these equations shows that the system is of the third order.

Stability. We shall determine the root loci from the denominator of equation (8.14), namely the characteristic equation:

$$s^3 + (a/\tau)s^2 + K[(a-1)/\tau]s + K[(a-1)/\tau^2] = 0 \qquad (8.16)$$

In Chapter 2, and more precisely in section 2.5, we studied the third-order loops. The root loci were plotted setting τ_3 as a parameter. If in equation (8.16), 1 is neglected in comparison with a, then τ_3 can be identified with $1/a$. If we use relationship (2.81), the identification gives

$$a = \omega_n(1 + 2\zeta) \qquad (8.17)$$

Let us recall equation (2.86c):

$$\frac{1}{\tau_2^2} = \frac{\omega_n^2}{(2\cos\Psi + 1)^2}$$

If we take the radius $R = 1/\tau_2$ as unity (section 2.5) and then we combine equations (8.17) and (2.86c), we obtain

$$a = (2\zeta + 1)(2\cos\Psi + 1) = (2\zeta + 1)^2 = (2\cos\Psi + 1)^2 \qquad (8.18)$$

Thus the value of the gain K' at the tangent point is

$$K' = 2\zeta + 1 \qquad (8.19)$$

namely, the square root of a.

Let us return to the root loci illustrated in Fig. 2.19 and set the value of the radius to 1 instead of 5.

Each locus curve will be marked with its corresponding parameter, namely a, and with the value of the gain K' at the tangent point. Regarding the root loci of Fig. 2.19 the angle Ψ has the following values:

$$\Psi = 0°$$
$$\Psi = 20°$$
$$\Psi = 45°$$

From equations (8.18) and (8.19) we calculate the corresponding values of a and K':

$$a = 9.00 \qquad K' = 3.00$$
$$a = 8.29 \qquad K' = 2.88$$
$$a = 5.83 \qquad K' = 2.41$$

Figure 8.21 represents the root-loci from which we shall study the stability.

We find the same conclusions as Gardner [7]. Actually, when $a > 9$ each root locus has two branches and the closed curve for high values of a tends to a circle whose radius is equal to 1. In that case, it is quite close to a second-order system.

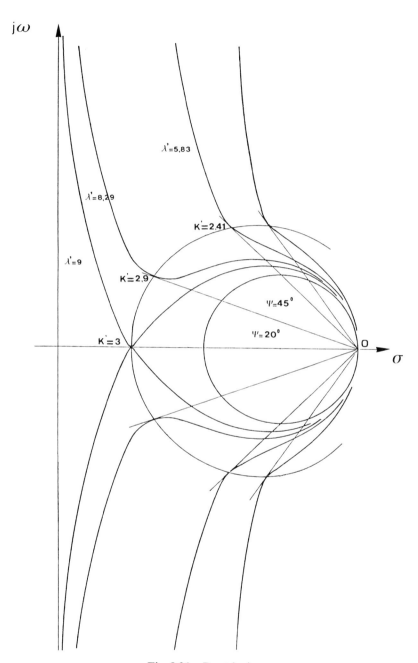

Fig. 8.21 Root loci.

If a is found to be between 9 and 5.83 the system is stable with an acceptable phase margin.

The value $a = 5.83$ corresponding to

$$\zeta = \frac{\sqrt{2}}{2}$$

$$\Phi_M = 45°$$

ensures a good compromise as far as the damping factor and the phase margin are concerned.

Tracking. The study is carried out from equation (8.15). The input signals are those of section 3.2 whose Laplace transforms are recalled below:

$$\Delta\Theta_{11}(s) = \frac{\Delta\phi}{s}$$

$$\Delta\Theta_{12}(s) = \frac{\Delta\omega}{s^2}$$

$$\Delta\Theta_{13}(s) = \frac{\Delta\dot{\omega}}{s^3}$$

If the final value theorem is applied to equation (8.15), we find that the error is null for the phase step as well as for the angular frequency step.

Regarding the application of an acceleration step, the error is found to be

$$\theta_{t \to \infty}(t) = \Delta\dot{\omega} \frac{a\tau}{K(a-1)} \qquad (8.20)$$

Since

$$a = 1 + \frac{C}{C_1}$$

$$K = \frac{K_0 I_p R}{2\pi}$$

relation (8.20) can be re-written as follows:

$$\theta_{t \to \infty}(t) = \frac{a}{a-1} \frac{2\pi C}{K_0 I_p} \Delta\dot{\omega} \qquad (8.21)$$

Since the calculated limit, in reality, is $\sin[\theta(t)]$, expression (8.21) approaches 1. Thus

$$1 = \frac{a}{a-1} \frac{2\pi C}{K_0 I_p} \Delta\dot{\omega} \qquad (8.22)$$

and we deduce

$$\Delta\dot\omega = \frac{a-1}{a}\frac{K_0 I_p}{2\pi C}$$

$$= \frac{a-1}{a}\frac{K}{RC}$$

$$= \frac{a-1}{a}\omega_n^2$$

Therefore,

1. if the linear variation of the angular frequency has a slope greater than

$$[(a-1)/a]\omega_n^2$$

the system unlocks, and
2. If, initially, the system is unlocked, capture is impossible if, simultaneously, the reference angular frequency slope behaviour is the same as mentioned above.

8.3 TECHNOLOGY OF FABRICATION

Semidigital PLLs silicon chips are made using CMOS, NMOS or bipolar processes.

According to the frequency required, one of these three processes will be used.

A very popular IC, the 4046, processed in CMOS, has been introduced by several semiconductor firms. It is very representative of semidigital PLLs.

Regarding bipolar ICs containing PLL functions the following logic families are normally used:

1. IIL (integrated injected logic);
2. ECL (emitter coupled logic);
3. miniwatt.

Philips Components introduces a large number of PLL circuits, incorporating many other features, for television, radio and compact disc applications.

Let us quote two commercial types. The first is a radio tuning frequency synthesizer, SAA 6057, covering the bands between 500 kHz and 150 MHz. The second is a television channel selection synthesizer, the SAA 5510, covering the bands between 64 MHz and 1.3 GHz.

9

Applications

The number of PLL applications is so large that it is impossible to cover all of them in one single chapter, and therefore we have limited them to only four but very important sectors:

1. radio,
2. television,
3. telephony, and
4. motors.

Before starting the study of any kind of application it is necessary to recall the principles on what it is based. That is why we have studied, thoroughly, a reduced number of topics, rather than showing a large number of schematics which may not be comprehensible to the reader who has not knowledge of the system.

9.1 RADIO (HERTZIAN TRANSMISSION)

9.1.1 Objective

Transmit a message from a point to another point (or several points) using as a transport carrier an electromagnetic wave.

9.1.2 Modulation

This operation allows the incorporation of a message into the transport vehicle, namely the carrier wave.

9.1.3 Transmission

The carrier wave and its message, by means of a transmitter and an aerial, are sent into space, most of the time in all directions, and occasionally in a unique direction.

The transmission takes place in the atmosphere as well as in the vacuum space.

9.1.4 Reception

The aerial together with its tuning circuit performs a rough selection of the signals within a certain frequency band. Once this pre-selection is carried out, the receiver amplifies the signals in its radio frequency (RF) stage; then it operates a frequency shift by means of a mixer, allowing the selection of only the desired carrier wave and the transport of its message with a lower and constant frequency. Such a frequency is called intermediate frequency (IF). It has been fixed at 455 kHz for amplitude modulation (AM) and at 10.7 MHz for FM. This frequency change is followed by an IF amplification. The next operation, the demodulation or detection, recovers the message and removes the IF carrier signal. Since the message audio signal is very weak it has to be pre-amplified and amplified. The last operation consists of converting the signal information back to its original form, namely sound waves, by means of the loudspeaker.

9.1.5 Superheterodyne receiver

Following the description of the signal radio processing in the preceding section, we are now able to propose a very general block diagram, for illustrative purposes, in Fig. 9.1. We shall see how a certain number of functions represented in the block diagram can be realized by means of PLL networks.

9.1.6 Amplitude modulation

The expression of a carrier wave has the following form:

$$f(t) = V_C \cos \omega_C t$$

The amplitude of the carrier is modulated by the message signal.

We shall proceed with a very simple case where the message is a signal sinusoidal signal whose angular frequency is ω_m and which is represented by the following electrical signal:

$$v = V_m \cos \omega_m t$$

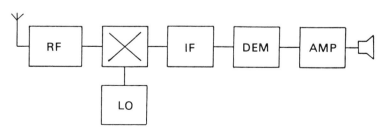

Fig. 9.1 Block diagram of a radio receiver.

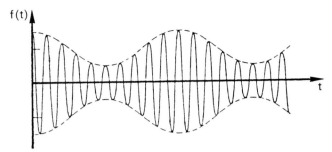

Fig. 9.2   Amplitude modulated carrier.

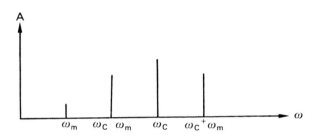

Fig. 9.3   Spectrum of the amplitude modulated carrier wave.

The expression of the modulated carrier is as follows

$$f(t) = V_C(1 + m \cos \omega_m t) \cos \omega_C t \qquad (9.1)$$

where m is the modulation factor or index. We then have

$$m = \frac{V_m}{V_C}$$

with the restrictive condition $m < 1$. Figure 9.2 is an illustration of the function $f(t)$.

The carrier frequency $\omega_C/2\pi$ has to be chosen so that the transmission is possible. The condition is that the modulating frequency of the message signal $\omega_m/2\pi$ should be small compared with the carrier frequency.

Using a very well-known trigonometric identity

$$\cos a \cos b = \tfrac{1}{2}[\cos(a + b) + \cos(a - b)]$$

the expression for the modulated carrier signal can be re-written:

$$f(t)V_C \cos \omega_C t + \frac{m}{2} V_C \cos(\omega_C + \omega_m)t + \frac{m}{2} V_C \cos(\omega_C - \omega_m)t \qquad (9.2)$$

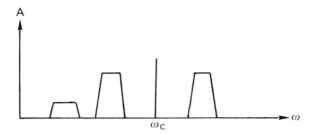

Fig. 9.4 AM spectrum with non-sinusoidal modulation.

From this the spectrum representation of the modulated carrier signal can be plotted as in Fig 9.3.

We notice that the carrier is unaffected by the modulation process, and therefore it does not carry any kind of information. On the contrary, the amplitudes of the upper and lower side angular frequencies $\omega_C + \omega_m$ and $\omega_C - \omega_m$ are proportional to the modulation index and we can imagine that it should be possible to transmit the message according to three different techniques provided that we have, at our disposal, the correct detectors:

1. 'straight' AM modulation;
2. double-sideband suppressed carrier (DSB–SC);
3. single-sideband suppressed carrier (SSB–SC).

The AM spectrum with non-sinusoidal modulation is more complex; it is continuous as illustrated in Fig. 9.4.

9.1.7 Frequency modulation (FM)

As in the case of AM transmission, in order to simplify, we shall assume a single sinusoidal modulating signal of the form

$$v = V_m \cos \omega_m t$$

The angular frequency deviation $\delta\omega(t)$ from the carrier angular frequency ω_C is directly proportional to the instantaneous amplitude of the modulating signal. We then have

$$\delta\omega(t) = k_m V_m \cos \omega_m t$$

The carrier signal is thus of the form

$$f(t) = V_C \cos \phi(t)$$

The instantaneous angular frequency is given by

$$\omega(t) = \frac{d\phi(t)}{dt} = \omega_C + \delta\omega(t)$$

where

$$\phi(t) = \omega_C t + \int_0^t \delta\omega(t)\,dt$$

$$= \omega_C t + k_m V_m \int_0^t \cos\omega_m t\,dt$$

$$= \omega_C t + \frac{K_m V_m}{\omega_m}\sin\omega_m t$$

Therefore

$$f(t) = V_C\left(\omega_C t + \frac{k_m V_m}{\omega_m}\sin\omega_m t\right)$$

Until the input of the detector, signal processing is roughly the same as for AM, but the intermediate frequency is 10.7 MHz. Before detection, FM requires a frequency–voltage conversion. There are several techniques to recover the modulating signal.

9.1.8 Intermediate frequency (IF)

As we have seen, after the RF amplification, a frequency shift is carried out by means of a mixer which multiplies the incoming signal with a signal produced by a local oscillator. A receiver based on this principle is called superheterodyne.

We shall see now, in a very simple case, how the frequency shift can be realized. Let

$$v_1 = V_1 \cos\omega_1 t$$

be the signal produced by the local oscillator. Since the mixer performs a multiplication, we have at its output

$$g(t) = AV_C(1 + m\cos\omega_m t)\cos\omega_C t\, V_1\cos\omega_1 t \qquad (9.3)$$

where $A(V^{-1})$ is the mixer gain.

Depending on the characteristics of the mixer, other terms apart from the product may be obtained at its output, but we shall neglect them.

Using the trigonometric identity, already applied, equation (9.3) can be rewritten as follows:

$$g(t) = A\frac{V_C V_1}{2}(1 + m\cos\omega_m t)[\cos(\omega_C + \omega_1)t + \cos(\omega_C - \omega_1)t] \qquad (9.4)$$

A low pass filter allows us to eliminate the angular frequency $\omega_C + \omega_1$ and we obtain

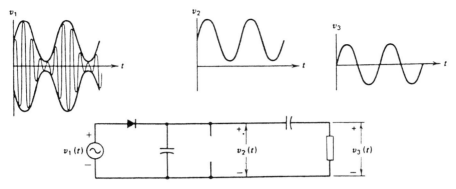

Fig. 9.5 Diode detector and its principle of operation [8].

$$g(t) = A\frac{V_C V_1}{2}(1 + m\cos\omega_m t)\cos(\omega_C - \omega_1)t \qquad (9.5)$$

From now on, the message is carried by a signal whose angular frequency is no longer ω_C but

$$f_i = \frac{\omega_i}{2\pi} = \frac{\omega_C - \omega_1}{2\pi}$$

The system is called infradyne if $\omega_1 < \omega_C$ and supradyne if $\omega_1 > \omega_C$. The IF has been fixed to 455 kHz. The mixer–oscillator stage is connected to an IF amplifier whose bandwidth is centred on 455 kHz.

9.1.9 AM demodulation

The simple circuit represented in Fig. 9.5 allows us to recover the modulating signal. Such a device is called an envelope detector. Nevertheless, if the transmission is of the suppressed carrier type demodulation is not possible with this detector.

9.1.10 FM demodulation

In section 1.2.2 a simple explanation was given to show how PLL demodulation works. There are several other means to demodulate FM signals but we do not intend to mention them since they are outside the scope of this book.

9.1.11 Superheterodyne radio functions feasible with PLLs

In three very specific fields PLL circuits favourably replace conventional systems:

1. tuners,
2. FM stereo demodulation, and
3. AM demodulation.

9.1.12 Tuners

(a) Conventional type

A very simple model will be described, in order to show how the conventional type is replaced with the PLL type.

Figure 9.6 represents a very simplified schematic of a standard tuner. Two tuned circuits are present: one is connected to the aerial in order to select the desired channel, the other is used to tune the frequency of the local oscillator. The tuner performs the following relationship:

$$|f_1 - f_C| = f_{IF}$$

(where f_1 and f_C, respectively, the local oscillator and carrier frequencies) by

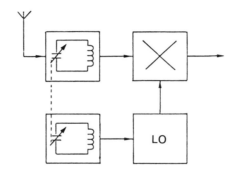

Fig. 9.6 Conventional tuner.

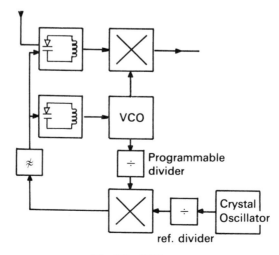

Fig. 9.7 PLL tuner.

means of two mechanically coupled air-cored capacitors, whose capacitance can cover a range between a few picofarads to about 500 pF. The tuning can also be obtained by means of a variable inductance ferrite-cored coil. In both cases the tuning is manual.

(b) PLL synthesizer type

The air-cored capacitors are replaced with variable-capacitance diodes which are controlled by the tuning voltage error (Fig. 9.7). The output of the pro-grammable frequency divider is compared with a crystal-controlled reference frequency (after having been divided by N). The result of the comparison, which represents the tuning error, is amplified and filtered before being used to modify the tuning voltage applied to the variable-capacitance diodes in the appropriate local oscillator tuned circuit and in the RF tuned circuit.

To cover the total range of frequencies the reference frequency must be low enough (that is why the quartz frequency is divided) in order to produce all the multiples required.

Numerical example: AM receiver

The following bands must be covered: MW–LW–SW. That is to say, the frequency must range from 148 kHz to 18 MHz.

Setting the reference frequency f_r equal to 1 kHz, the programmable divider range must generate all the numbers between 148 and 18 000. The reception being supradyne, the local oscillator frequency is

$$f_1 = f_{IF} + f_C = 455\,kHz + f_C$$

The frequency range of the local oscillator should be from 603 kHz to 18 455 kHz.

A 15 bit counter allows all the necessary division factors for such an applica-tion to be obtained:

1. 9 bits are necessary to obtain 512;
2. 15 bits are necessary to obtain 32 768.

A 14 bit counter would have not permit us to reach the correct divisor, and therefore it would not have been possible to reach 18 MHz. with our choices, the receiver is able to select all carriers between 57 kHz and 32 313 kHz.

9.1.13 PLL FM demodulation

Although the PLL technique looks attractive, very few radio makers have adopted it for FM demodulation. As a matter of fact, there is no benefit regarding cost and, as far as performance is concerned, is no real advantage.

9.1.14 FM stereo demodulation

In stereo broadcasting, the left (L) and right (R) signals are not directly transmitted. As a matter of fact, for compatibility reasons, namely to allow owners of mono radios to receive correct transmissions, the sum $L + R$ is transmitted directly. The difference $L - R$ is transmitted by means of a subcarrier of the DSB–SC type.

The frequency of the subcarrier is 38 kHz. Simultaneously, a 19 kHz pilot signal phase coherent with the subcarrier is transmitted to synchronize the subcarrier oscillator of the receiver with the subcarrier oscillator of the transmitter.

The complete spectrum is illustrated in Fig. 9.8.

The spectrum shows why the pilot signal is transmitted with a frequency of 19 kHz, instead of 38 kHz. Indeed, if that frequency had been chosen it would have been necessary to use a very critical filter to recover the pilot signal, owing to the sidebands which are only twice 30 kHz apart.

In a mono receiver, since the FM spectrum is limited to 15 kHz, the pilot signal falls outside of it.

Regarding the stereo receiver, it coherently demodulates the $R + L$ and $R - L$ signals; then, by adding and subtracting them, the R and L signals are obtained.

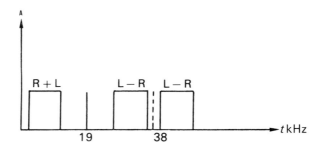

Fig. 9.8 FM stereo spectrum.

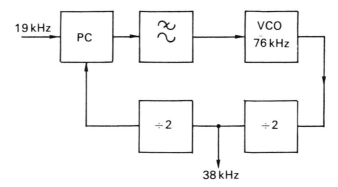

Fig. 9.9 Stereo subcarrier generation.

Figure 9.9 shows how the PLL regenerates the 38 kHz subcarrier from the pilot signal.

9.1.15 Synchronous, or homodyne, reception

Contrary to superheterodyne reception there is no frequency shift. Therefore, the local oscillator must be adjusted to exactly the same frequency as the carrier. This application gave birth in 1932 to PLL [9] systems.

9.1.16 Principle

The coherent demodulation is based on the following principle: if the carrier of the incoming signal is multiplied by a local signal whose frequency is the same as the carrier, after filtering, the modulating signal is recovered. The block diagram in Fig. 9.10 illustrates the coherent demodulation.

Let equation (9.1) be multiplied by

$$r(t) = R \cos(\omega_C t + \phi)$$

We obtain

$$x(t) = V_C R(1 + m \cos \omega_m t) \cos \omega_C t \, R \cos(\omega_C + \phi)$$

which can be re-written as follows:

$$x(t) = V_C R(1 + m \cos \omega_m t)[\cos(2\omega_C t + \phi) + \cos \phi]$$

Filtering eliminates the component whose angular frequency is $2\omega_C t$, and we obtain

$$y(t) = V_C R(1 + m \cos \omega_m t) \cos \phi$$

namely the modulating signal.

9.1.17 Coherent demodulation with a PLL

If the VCO produces a signal out of phase by $\pi/2$ when the reference signal frequency is equal to its free-running frequency, $\cos \phi$ is equal to 0 and demodulation is not possible. Therefore, it is necessary to add a $\pi/2$ phase network

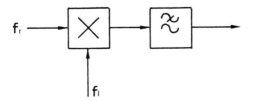

Fig. 9.10 Block diagram for coherent demodulation.

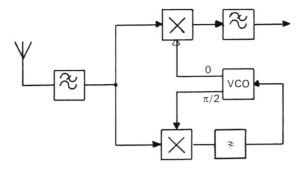

Fig. 9.11   Block diagram of a PLL synchronous receiver.

in the system to compensate for the normal phase shift. Figure 9.11 illustrates a block diagram of an AM receiver.

9.1.18   Advantages

The main advantages are

1. simplicity,
2. possibility of designing a one-chip radio, since its main functions can be integrated, and
3. good selectivity when the signal-to-noise ratio is low.

9.1.19   Practical realization

A phase locked AM receiver is described in the Signetics [10] application manual, based on the block diagram of Fig. 9.11. IC 561 B is used together with a rather small number of peripheral components (Fig. 9.12). If its operation range is to be from 550 kHz to 1.6 MHz the components of Fig. 9.12 should have the following values:

$$C_Y = 135\,\text{pF}, \ R_Y = 3000\,\Omega, \ C_B = C_C = 0.1\,\mu\text{F}.$$

Tuning may be accomplished in several ways. The simplest one is to use a variable capacitor between pins 2 and 3 whose value may be obtained from the following formula:

$$\frac{300\,\text{pF}}{f_C}$$

where f_C is the carrier frequency expressed in megahertz.

Good performance can be obtained with a powerful aerial and a good ground. A broadband untuned RF amplifier may inprove the operation but care has to be taken not to saturate the phase comparator of the integrated circuit (input signal amplitude should not exceed 0.5 V r.m.s.).

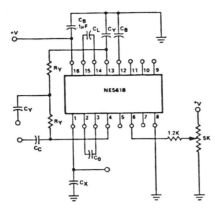

Fig. 9.12 AM receiver [10].

9.2 TELEVISION

Owing to the complexity of TV electronics, only two applications will be studied which will not require a profound knowledge of television electronics. The first one is related to tuning and the second one to line and frame synchronization.

9.2.1 PLL tuning

Television tuning may be accomplished by PLL synthesizing. Frequency selection is obtained by means of a programmable divider. This application is the same as for radio, only frequencies are different, and therefore the block diagram of Fig. 9.7 is still valid.

As for radio, the reference frequency must be small enough and the programmable divider sufficiently complex so that all the necessary multiplies of the reference frequency can be obtained.

The most suitable counter to do the job is the so-called Swallow counter. The block diagram of Fig. 9.13 illustrates its principle.

(a) Swallow counter operation

The circuit possesses a prescaler which can divide either by P or by $P + 1$. Blocks C_1 and C_2 are two down-counters whose output is high when they are set to any number but 0, and which goes low when they are set to 0.

To start with, the counters C_1 and C_2 are respectively set to N_1 and N_2 with the condition $N_2 < N_1$. Then the prescaler divides by $P + 1$. As soon as C_2 stores a 0 its output goes low, the counter is off and the prescaler is forced to divide by P. Counter C_1 will continue to down count and when it reaches 0 its output goes low and both counters are then reloaded.

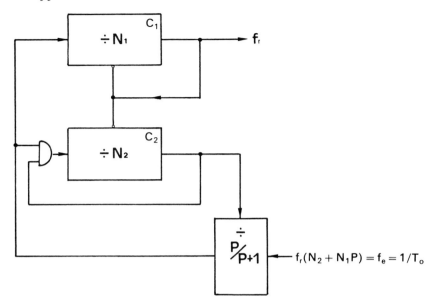

Fig. 9.13   Swallow counter.

Let T_0 be the signal period produced by the oscillator. At the prescaler output, we then have

$$T_0(P + 1)$$

The duration until C_2 is set to 0 will then be

$$N_2 T_0(P + 1)$$

Therefore, the period of the prescaler output signal is

$$T_0 P$$

and the down-counting of C_1 will last

$$T_0 P(N_1 - N_2)$$

Thus, the cycle period is

$$N_2 T_0(P + 1) + T_0 P(N_1 - N_2) = T_0(N_2 + N_1 P)$$

and the frequency of the signal produced by C_1 is

$$f = \frac{1}{T_0(N_2 + N_1 P)} = \frac{f_e}{N_2 + N_1 P}$$

The total division ratio is

$$N_T = N_2 + N_1 P \tag{9.6}$$

Let f_r be a divided-down stable crystal frequency reference. We then have

$$f_r = \frac{f_1}{N_T}$$

(b)   Channel selection

We shall determine the limits of a programmable divider dictated by a minimal step size of 40 kHz and a frequency range from 40 MHz to 1300 MHz. Therefore, if we divide these frequencies by 40 kHz, we find the ratio limits of the programmable divider, namely 1000 and 32 500.

We obtain a number close to the upper limit by multiplying 1024 by 32 which gives 32 768. Using equation (9.6), we select $P = 32$ and $N_1 = 1024$. If this last number is replaced by 1023 we can use a 10 bit counter.

Regarding the lower limit it is given by $N_T = 0 + N_1 \times 32$; thus we set $N_1 = 31$, whose product with 32 is equal to 992. Since the lowest value of N_1 must be larger or equal to the largest value of N_2, this last value must not exceed 32. Therefore, a 5 bit counter will do the job, since it can count to 31. Applying equation (9.6), we find the maximum division ratio, namely

$$N_T = 31 + 1023 \times 32 = 32\,767$$

Let us multiply 992 and 32 767 by $f_r = 40$ kHz in order to evaluate the frequency range; we find 39.68 MHz and 1310.68 MHz. Therefore, the specifications we were looking for are fulfilled.

9.2.2   Pulse generator for line and frame synchronization

The transmission standards used in Europe for television are as follows: scanning rate 625 lines per frame, 25 frames per second, consisting of two interlaced

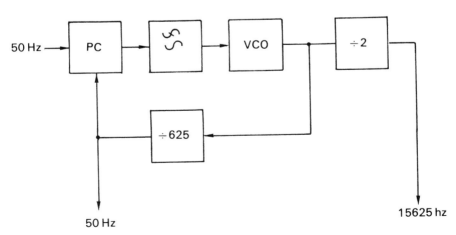

Fig. 9.14   Synchronization generator.

fields, each having 312.5 lines. There are 50 fields transmitted per second which corresponds to the power line frequency.

The horizontal line frequency is then 625×25 Hz, i.e. 15 625 Hz. Therefore we have to synthesize 50 and 15 625 in order to obtain the synchronizing pulses for scanning.

The PLL will have a reference signal whose frequency will be 50 Hz. Since the line frequency is not divisible by 50, we shall double it, giving 31 250 Hz. Therefore, the VCO will oscillate at that frequency and it will be easy to divide it by 2. The block diagram of the PLL network is represented in Fig. 9.14.

9.3   FAST SHIFT KEYING (FSK) DEMODULATION

This system is used in modems.

9.3.1   Principle

Binary data are transmitted via a carrier which is shifted between two present frequencies: the lower frequency represents a 0 and the higher represents a 1 (Fig. 9.15).

9.3.2   Demodulation

Demodulation may be represented with the rotating vector (Fig. 9.16).

The position of point H_1 corresponds to bit 0 and the position of point H_2 to bit 1. We jump from one point to the other every time an angular frequency step is applied. The projections of vectors $\overrightarrow{OH_0}$ and $\overrightarrow{OH_1}$ along the horizontal axis represent the demodulated voltages. Figure 9.17 represents the demodulated voltages versus time.

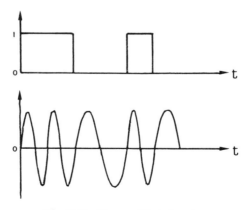

Fig. 9.15   Transmitted signals.

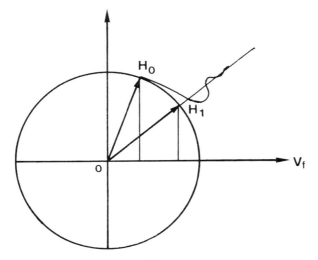

Fig. 9.16 FSK demodulation.

When studying a project two things are important: the deviation between the two frequencies and the damping factor of the network. Both may unlock the PLL (Chapter 3).

Many PLL ICs are designed for FSK projects, in particular the 565, whose applications were mentioned at the end of Chapter 7.

9.4 SPEED CONTROL OF DC MOTORS

9.4.1 Conventional speed control

Figure 9.18 represents a classical scheme. The set point for the motor speed is adjusted by means of a potentiometer. The motor shaft speed is measured with a tachometer which delivers a voltage proportional to the motor speed. This voltage is subtracted from the voltage applied to the servo amplifier controlling

Fig. 9.17 Demodulation signals.

the current of the induced coil. As long as this difference is maintained constant the speed of the motor remains constant.

9.4.2   Transfer function of the motor

Let us determine the transfer function of the motor from the following characteristics: J, the inertia momentum of the motor and its load; f, the viscous friction coefficient; r, l, the resistance and self-inductance of the inductor coil; K_M, the motor torque coefficient; K_1, the back-electromotive force coefficient. Let v_e and i be, respectively, the applied motor voltage and the current feeding the motor.

The equations of the motor are

$$v_e = ri + l\frac{di}{dt} + K_1\frac{d\theta}{dt}$$

$$K_M i = J\frac{d^2\theta}{dt^2} + f\frac{d\theta}{dt}$$

Applying the Laplace transform, we find

$$V_E(s) = rI(s) + slI(s) + sK_1\theta(s)$$
$$K_M I = Js^2\Theta(s) + fs\Theta(s)$$

from which the motor transfer function is obtained:

$$\frac{\Theta(s)}{V_E(s)} = \frac{K_M}{Jls^3 + (Jr + fl)s^2 + (rf + K_M K_1)s}$$

Assuming that l and f are negligible, we find

$$\frac{\Theta(s)}{V_E(s)} = \frac{K_M}{Jrs^2 + K_M K_1 s} = \frac{1}{K_1 s}\frac{1}{Jrs/K_M K_1 + 1}$$

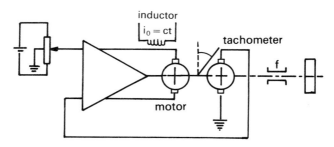

Fig. 9.18   Sketch of the motor.

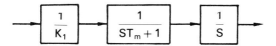

Fig. 9.19   Block diagram of the motor.

Setting

$$\frac{Jr}{K_M K_1} = T_m$$

we obtain

$$\frac{\Theta(s)}{V_E(s)} = \frac{1}{K_1 s} \frac{1}{T_m s + 1} \tag{9.7}$$

from which we can represent the block diagram of the motor (Fig. 9.19).

9.4.3   PLL speed control

Setting $1/K_1 = K_e$ in equation (9.7), the term K_e/s appears as the transfer function of a VCO and

$$\frac{1}{T_m s + 1}$$

as the transfer function of a filter of type 1.

   Now if we are able to measure the motor speed and to obtain from it an electrical signal the sketch of Fig. 9.18 may represent a block diagram of a PLL motor speed control. The three-state PC, charge pump and *RC* filter are necessary for the following reasons:

1. tracking requires frequency error between the input signals, and
2. constant speed requires phase error between the input signals.

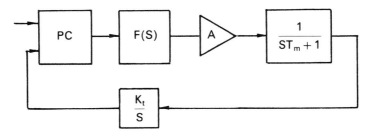

Fig. 9.20   PLL speed control block diagram.

Separating the error commands has another advantage. The capture range when this method is used is limited only by the characteristics of the controlled variable. For instance, in a conventional PLL the VCO frequency will operate within its full range. Regarding the motor speed control this means that motors can be controlled from stand still to any desired speed under total control of the loop.

(a)   Motor speed measurement

Several techniques can be used. The most common is to fix a sector disk on the shaft of the motor and to use a fork-shaped optocoupler which senses the chopped light beam emitted by a LED. A square-wave electrical signal is obtained which is cleaned with a Schmitt trigger. Another possible technique is to fix on a disk having, instead of sectors, some magnetic ferrites and to sense their presence by means of a Hall integrated circuit which also contains an amplifier and a Schmitt trigger.

9.4.4 Study of PLL controlled speed

As already mentioned, the most appropriate PC for this application is the three-state type associated with a charge-pump and a RC filter. It was shown in section 8.2 that this network was equivalent to a phase comparator whose gain factor would be $K_d = I_p R/2\pi$ combined with a type 3 filter whose two resistors have the same resistance.

Taking into account the preceding results we can now illustrate in Fig. 9.21 the block diagram, in the frequency domain, of the PLL speed control system. For reasons of simplicity we have supposed that the disk has only a sector or a magnetic ferrite.

A close look at the block diagram shows that the system is equivalent to a PLL network with a type 4 filter; therefore the loop is of the third order and we can apply the results we established in section 2.5.

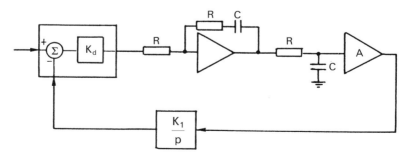

Fig. 9.21   Block diagram of a PLL speed control motor: $R'C' = T_m$.

Let us recall equation (2.62), i.e.

$$s^3 + \frac{1}{\tau_3}s^2 + \frac{K_v\tau_2}{\tau_1\tau_3}s + \frac{K_v}{\tau_1\tau_3} = 0$$

and look for analogies taking into account the variables indicated in Fig. 9.21. We have

$$T_m = \tau_3$$

$$\frac{K_v\tau_2}{\tau_1\tau_3} = \frac{K}{T_m} \quad (\tau_1 = \tau_2 = RC)$$

$$\frac{K_v}{\tau_1\tau_3} = \frac{K}{RCT_m}$$

where

$$K = K_e I_p \frac{R}{2\pi}$$

and we obtain the characteristic equation

$$s^3 + \frac{1}{T_m}s^2 + \frac{K}{T_m}s + \frac{K}{T_m RC} = 0 \qquad (9.8)$$

9.4.5 Numerical example

Let us consider a motor controlled by means of a voltage applied to the induced coil, whose characteristics are

$$K_1 = \frac{1}{K_e} = 0.063 \text{ V s rad}^{-1}$$

$$J = 1.5 \times 10^{-5} \text{ kg m}^2$$

$$K = 0.4 \text{ N m A}^{-1}$$

$$r = 530\,\Omega$$

$$f \approx 0$$

$$l \approx 0$$

A power amplifier precedes the motor whose voltage gain is 6.35. The disk that ensures counting has only one ferrite element.

Let us calculate T_m; we obtain

$$T_m = \frac{Jr}{KK_1} = 50 \text{ ms}$$

If we return to example 1 given in section 2.5.3, the characteristic equation is

$$s^3 + 20s^2 + 166s + 572 = 0$$

Identifying the coefficients of equation (9.8), we have

$$\frac{K}{T_m} = 166$$

$$\frac{K}{T_m RC} = 572$$

and then we obtain

$$K = 8.3 \, \text{rad s}^{-1}$$
$$RC = 0.29 \, \text{s}$$
$$\frac{K}{RC} = 28.6$$

which are the results obtained from the application of example 1. Therefore

$$K = K_e I_p \frac{R}{2\pi} = 8.3 \, \text{rad s}^{-1}$$

With a current I_p equal to $700 \, \mu\text{A}$, we find $R = 29 \, \text{k}\Omega$ and $C = 0.1 \, \mu\text{F}$.

Appendix A   The Laplace transform

A.1   DEFINITION

The Laplace transformation associates a given function $f(t)$ with a second function $F(s)$ so that

$$F(s) = L[f(t)] = \int_0^\infty f(t)e^{-st}\,dt$$

where t is a real variable, $f(t)$ is a real function of t, $f(t) = 0$ for $t < 0$, and $F(s)$ is a function of s, where $s = \sigma + j\omega$.

$F(s)$ is called the Laplace transform of $f(t)$.

A.2   PROPERTIES

A.2.1   Linearity

Let f_1 and f_2 be two functions and a_1 and a_2 two constants. Consider the Laplace transform of their linear form

$$a_1 f_1 + a_2 f_2$$

namely

$$\int_0^\infty [a_1 f_1(t) + a_2 f_2(t)]e^{-st}\,dt$$

We obtain

$$\int_0^\infty [a_1 f_1(t) + a_2 f_2(t)]e^{-st}\,dt = a_1 \int_0^\infty f_1(t)^{-st}\,dt + a_2 \int_0^\infty f_2(t)e^{-st}\,dt$$

which can be re-written as follows:

$$L[a_1 f_1(t) + a_2 f_2(t)] = a_1 L[f_1(t)] + a_2 L[f_2(t)]$$

A.2.2   Shifting theorem

Consider a function $f(t - \tau)$ null for $t < \tau$. Its Laplace transform is

$$L[f(t - \tau)] = \int_\tau^\infty f(t - \tau)e^{-st}\,dt$$

Setting $t - \tau = T$ and substituting in the integral yields

$$\int_0^\infty f(T)e^{-s(T + \tau)}\,d(T + \tau) = e^{-s\tau}\int_0^\infty f(T)e^{-sT}\,dt$$

$$= e^{-s\tau}L[f(t)]$$

Therefore, a shift to the right of τ in the time domain corresponds to multiplication by $e^{-s\tau}$ in the complex frequency domain.

A.2.3   Differentiation in the time domain

Consider the function $df(t)/dt$, null for $t < 0$. Its Laplace transform is

$$L\left[\frac{df(t)}{dt}\right] = \int_0^\infty \frac{df(t)}{dt}e^{-st}\,dt$$

Integrating by parts, we obtain

$$\int_0^\infty \frac{df(t)}{dt}e^{-st}\,dt = [f(t)e^{-st}]_0^\infty - \int_0^\infty f(t)\frac{de^{-st}}{dt}\,dt$$

$$= -f(0^+) + s\int_0^\infty f(t)e^{-st}\,dt$$

$$= sL[f(t)] - f(0^+)$$

where $f(0^+)$ is the initial condition, namely the value of $f(t)$ when t approaches 0 from positive values.

Next let us repeat the differentiation a second time; we find

$$\int_0^\infty \left[\frac{d^2 f(t)}{dt^2}\right]e^{-st}\,dt = sL\left(\frac{df(t)}{dt}\right) - \frac{df(0^+)}{dt}$$

$$= s^2 L[f(t)] - sf(0^+) - \frac{df(0^+)}{dt}$$

A.2.4   Integration in the time domain

Let $\int f(t)\,dt$ be a time function. Its Laplace transform is

$$L\left[\int f(t)\,dt\right] = \int_0^\infty \left[\int f(t)\,dt\right]e^{-st}\,dt$$

Integrating by parts we find that

$$\int_0^\infty \left[\int f(t)\,dt \right] e^{-st}\,dt = -\frac{1}{s} \left[\int [f(t)\,dt] e^{-st} \right]_0^\infty + \frac{1}{s} \int_0^\infty f(t) e^{-st}\,dt$$

$$L\left[\int f(t)\,dt \right] = \frac{1}{s} L[f(t)] + \frac{1}{s} f^{(-1)}(0^+)$$

where $f^{(-1)}(0^+)$ is the initial value of $f(t)\,dt$.

A.2.5   Unit-step, unit-impulse and unit-ramp functions

The unit-step function u_e is defined as follows:

$$u_e(t) = 0 \quad \text{for} \quad t < 0$$
$$u_e(t) = 1 \quad \text{for} \quad t > 0$$

It is plotted in Fig. A.1. Let us determine its Laplace transform:

$$\int_0^\infty u_e(t) e^{-st}\,dt = \left[-\frac{1}{s} e^{-st} \right]_0^\infty = \frac{1}{s}$$

If the amplitude of the unit-step function is a then the Laplace transform is a/s.

The unit-impulse function u_i is defined as the derivative of the unit-step function; therefore we have

$$u_i(t) = 0 \quad \text{for} \quad t \neq 0$$
$$u_i(t) = \infty \quad \text{for} \quad t = 0$$

and

$$\int_0^\infty u_i(t) e^{-st}\,dt = s\frac{1}{s} = 1$$

thus

$$\int_{0^-}^{0^+} u_i(t)\,dt = 1$$

A specific example may be given by considering a rectangle pulse of duration

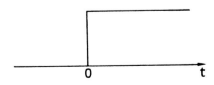

Fig. A.1   Unit-step function.

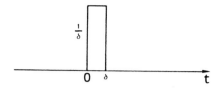

Fig. A.2   Unit-impulse function.

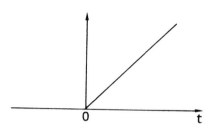

Fig. A.3   Ramp function.

δ and amplitude $1/\delta$. If now δ approaches 0, in the limit, the rectangle is the unit-impulse function. Figure A.2 illustrates the function.

The unit-ramp function $u_r(t)$ is defined as

$$u_r(t) = 0 \quad \text{for} \quad t < 0$$
$$u_r(t) = t \quad \text{for} \quad t > 0$$

and is represented in Fig. A.3. In order to obtain its Laplace transform, the following calculation is made

$$\int_0^\infty t e^{-st}\,dt = \left[-\frac{1}{s} t e^{-st} \right]_0^\infty + \frac{1}{s} e^{-st}\,dt$$

$$= 0 - \frac{1}{s^2} [e^{-st}]_0^\infty = \frac{1}{s^2}$$

The same result can be obtained if we remark that the unit-ramp function is the integral of the unit-step function. Then it suffices to multiply $1/s$ by $1/s$.

If the unit-ramp function has a slope equal to k its Laplace transform is multiplied by k, and therefore we find k/s^2.

A.2.6   Application to some common functions

Consider the function $e^{-\alpha t}$; its Laplace transform is

$$L[e^{-\alpha t}] = \int_0^\infty e^{-\alpha t} e^{-st}\,dt = -\frac{1}{\alpha + p} [e^{-(\alpha + s)t}]_0^\infty = \frac{1}{\alpha + s}$$

Next let us calculate the Laplace transform of the function $\sin \omega t$:

$$L[\sin \omega t] = \int_0^\infty \sin \omega t \, e^{-st} \, dt$$

Now

$$\sin \omega t = \frac{e^{j\omega t} - e^{-j\omega t}}{2j}$$

Thus

$$L[\sin \omega t] = \frac{1}{2j} \int_0^\infty (e^{j\omega t - st} - e^{-j\omega t - st}) \, dt$$

$$L[\sin \omega t] = \frac{1}{2j} \left\{ \frac{1}{j\omega - s} [e^{j\omega t - st}]_0^\infty + \frac{1}{j\omega + s} [e^{-j\omega t - st}]_0^\infty \right\}$$

Since

$$s = \sigma + j\omega$$

we have

$$L[\sin \omega t] = \frac{1}{2j} \left\{ \frac{1}{j\omega - s} [e^{-\sigma t}]_0^\infty + \frac{1}{j\omega + s} [e^{-(\sigma + 2j\omega)t}]_0^\infty \right\}$$

and

$$L[\sin \omega t] = -\frac{1}{2j} \left(\frac{1}{-s + j\omega} + \frac{1}{s + j\omega} \right) = \frac{\omega}{s^2 + \omega^2}$$

Next we calculate the Laplace transform of the function $\cos \omega t$, namely

$$L[\cos \omega t] = \int_0^\infty \cos \omega t \, e^{-st} \, dt$$

and since

$$\cos \omega t = \frac{e^{j\omega t} + e^{-j\omega t}}{2}$$

we obtain

$$L[\cos \omega t] = \frac{1}{2} \int_0^\infty (e^{j\omega t - st} + e^{-j\omega t - st}) \, dt$$

$$L[\cos \omega t] = \frac{1}{2} \left\{ \frac{1}{j\omega - s} [e^{j\omega t - st}]_0^\infty - \frac{1}{j\omega + s} [e^{-j\omega t - st}]_0^\infty \right\}$$

Substituting

$$s = \sigma + j\omega$$

we find

$$L[\cos \omega t] = \frac{1}{2}\left\{ \frac{1}{j\omega - s}[e^{-\sigma t}]_0^\infty - \frac{1}{j\omega + s}[e^{-(\sigma + 2j\omega)t}]_0^\infty \right\}$$

and

$$L[\cos \omega t] = \frac{1/(s - j\omega) + 1/(s + j\omega)}{2} = \frac{s}{s^2 + \omega^2}$$

A.2.7 Laplace transform table

Frequency complex domain	Time domain
1	$u_i(t)$
$\dfrac{1}{s}$	$u_e(t)$
$\dfrac{1}{s^2}$	t
$\dfrac{1}{s^3}$	$\dfrac{t^2}{2}$
$\dfrac{1}{s + a}$	e^{-at}
$\dfrac{s}{(s + a)^2}$	$(1 - at)e^{-at}$
$\dfrac{1}{(s + a)(s + b)}$	$\dfrac{e^{-at} - e^{-bt}}{b - a}$
$\dfrac{s + a}{(s + b)(s + c)}$	$\dfrac{(b - a)e^{-bt} - (c - a)e^{-ct}}{b - c}$
$\dfrac{s + a}{(s + b)^2}$	$[1 + (a - b)t]e^{-bt}$
$\dfrac{s + k}{s(s + a)(s + b)}$	$\dfrac{k}{ab} + \dfrac{k - a}{a(a - b)}e^{-at} + \dfrac{k - b}{b(b - a)}e^{-bt}$
$\dfrac{s(s + d)}{(s + a)(s + b)(s + c)}$	$\dfrac{a(a - d)e^{-at}}{(b - a)(c - a)} + \dfrac{b(b - d)e^{-bt}}{(a - b)(c - b)} + \dfrac{c(c - d)e^{-ct}}{(a - c)(b - c)}$

A.2.8 Initial and final values

Every time we want to know the initial value $f(0)$ of a function $f(t)$ or its final value $f(\infty)$, the following theorems are applied:

$$f(t)_{t \to 0} = \lim sL[f(t)]_{s \to \infty}$$
$$f(t)_{t \to \infty} = \lim sL[f(t)]_{s \to 0}$$

Appendix B   Notions on feedback and control systems

B.1   DEFINITION

B.1.1   Linear system

A system is said to be linear if the output or response function is related to the input or excitation function by a linear differential equation whose coefficients are constant and real. The equation is thus of the following form

$$a_n \frac{d^n s(t)}{dt^n} + a_{n-1} \frac{d^{n-1} s(t)}{dt^{n-1}} + \cdots + a_1 \frac{ds(t)}{dt} + a_0 s(t)$$

$$= b_m \frac{d^m e(t)}{dt^m} + b_{m-1} \frac{d^{m-1} e(t)}{dt^{m-1}} + \cdots + b_1 \frac{de(t)}{dt} + b_0$$

where $e(t)$ is the input signal and $s(t)$ the output signal (Fig. B.1).

B.1.2   Feedback system

A feedback system is designed to reduce, by itself, the error between the desired response and the response which is really obtained. Feedback is obtained by applying the output, or rather part of it, at the input. A feedback system is represented in Fig. B.2.

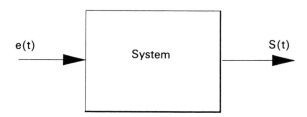

Fig. B.1   Responses of a system to an excitation.

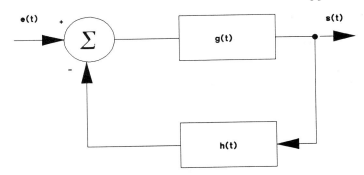

Fig. B.2   Feedback system.

B.2   RESPONSE OF LINEAR SYSTEMS

B.2.1   Transfer function

In principle, the differential equation related to a linear system allows us to calculate the response to an excitation.

Taking the Laplace transform of both sides of the equation given in section A.2.1(a), we obtain

$$(a_n s^n + a_{n-1} + \cdots + a_1 s + a_0)S(s) = (b_m s^m + b_{m-1} s^{m-1} + \cdots + b_1 s + b_0)E(s)$$

where $S(s)$ and $E(s)$ are, respectively, the Laplace transforms of $s(t)$ and $e(t)$. Therefore, we have

$$S(s) = \frac{b_m s^m + b_{m-1} s^{m-1} + \cdots + b_1 s + b_0}{a_n s^n + a_{n-1} s^{n-1} + \cdots + a_1 s + a_0} E(s)$$

The rational function

$$T(s) = \frac{S(s)}{E(s)}$$

is defined as the transfer function of the system. Two cases will be considered: $s = \sigma + j\omega$ and $s = j\omega$. The first case corresponds to any excitation and the second to a sinusoidal excitation.

B.2.2   Application

We consider the response to an unit-impulse function:

$$e(t) = u_i(t)$$

Therefore, the transfer function of a system initially at rest is the Laplace transform response to a unit-impulse function.

B.2.3   Poles and zeros

According to d'Alembert's theorem any equation of any degree whose coefficients are real (or complex) has always at least a real (or complex) root. It can also be stated that any equation of degree m has exactly m roots, either real or else complex. Therefore, the transfer function $T(s)$ can be written as follows:

$$T(s) = \frac{b_m(s - z_1)(s - z_2)\cdots(s - z_m)}{a_n(s - s_1)(s - s_2)\cdots(s - s_n)}$$

We shall restrict ourselves to $n > m$; the numbers $z_1, \ldots, z_m$ are called zeros of the transfer function and the numbers $s_1, \ldots, s_n$ are called the poles of the transfer function.

Assuming, in order to simplify, that all the poles are simple ones, namely of order 1, then we can expand the denominator of the transfer function $T(s)$ into partial fractions, that is to say in the following form:

$$T(s) = \frac{A_1}{s - s_1} + \frac{A_2}{s - s_2} + \cdots + \frac{A_n}{s - s_n}$$

$$= \sum_{i=1}^{i=n} \frac{A_i}{s - s_i}$$

A_i is called the residue related to pole s_i; it can be calculated from the expression

$$A_i = [(s - s_i)T(s)]_{s=s_i}$$

Let us calculate its response to the unit-impulse function $u_i(t)$, whose Laplace transform is 1. We have

$$S(s) = T(s) \times 1$$

$$= \frac{A_1}{s - s_1} + \frac{A_2}{s - s_2} + \cdots + \frac{A_n}{s - s_n}$$

From the table of Laplace transform $A_i/(s - s_i)$ correspond to $A_i e^{s_i t}$. Therefore, we have

$$s(t) = A_1 e^{s_1 t} + A_2 e^{s_2 t} + \cdots + A_n e^{s_n t}$$

Since we assumed that the coefficients a_i and b_j were real, the roots are either real or complex conjugate.

Note. To represent the location of poles and zeros in the complex s plane it is common practice to use, respectively, crosses and circles. The complex s plane is split into two semiplanes, the left half and the right half, separated by the imaginary axis $j\omega$. The real axis is reserved to σ.

Let us return to the response $s(t)$ in the time domain due to the application of an unit-impulse function. Two cases will be considered.

(a) First case: poles are real

The locations are represented with crosses along the real axis σ.

If s_i is negative, then the corresponding pole is located in the left-hand half of the complex s plane, along the real axis. Therefore, if t increases $e^{s_i t}$ decreases and approaches zero when t approaches infinity. Since the response will have the same behaviour, we obtain

$$s(t) = \sum_{i=1}^{i=n} A_i e^{s_i t}$$

On the contrary, if s_i is positive, the cross which represents it is located in the right-hand half of the s plane, along the real axis. In this case $e^{s_i t}$ increases when t increases and approaches infinity with t.

In Figs. B.3(a) and B.4(a) are represented, in the complex s plane, the different situations when the poles are real. Figures B.3(b) and B.4(b) represent the response related to these poles.

(b) Second case: poles are complex conjugate

Since the coefficients A_i are also complex, we have

$$s_i = \sigma + j\omega_i$$
$$A_i = a_i + jb_i$$

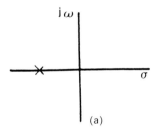
(a)

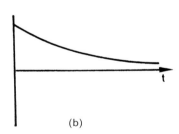
(b)

Fig. B.3 (a) Negative real pole. (b) Response: decreasing impulse.

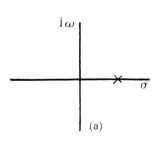
(a)

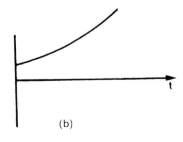
(b)

Fig. B.4 (a) Positive real pole. (b) Response: increasing impulse.

From this we obtain the response

$$s(t) = L^{-1}\left[\frac{A_i}{s - s_i}\right] = A_i e^{s_i t}$$
$$= (a_i + jb_i)e^{(\sigma_i + j\omega_i)t}$$

which can be re-written as follows:

$$s(t) = (a_i + jb_i)e^{\sigma_i t}(\cos \omega_i t + j \sin \omega_i t)$$

Next we consider the corresponding complex conjugate, that is to say

$$s_i^* = \sigma_i - j\omega_i$$
$$A_i^* = a_i - jb_i$$

We then have

$$L^{-1}\left[\frac{A_i^*}{s - s_i^*}\right] = A_i^* e^{s_i^* t}$$

Therefore, taking into account the two poles, we obtain

$$s(t) = 2e^{\sigma_i t}(a_i \cos \omega_i t - b_i \sin \omega_i t)$$

Then setting

$$\cos \phi_i = \frac{a_i}{(a_i^2 + b_i^2)^{1/2}}$$

$$\sin \phi_i = \frac{b_i}{(a_i^2 + b_i^2)^{1/2}}$$

$$\tan \phi_i = \frac{b_i}{a_i}$$

and substituting in the preceding equation, we obtain

$$s(t) = 2(a_i^2 + b_i^2)^{1/2}e^{\sigma_i t}(\cos \phi_i \cos \omega_i t - \sin \phi_i \sin \omega_i t)$$
$$s(t) = 2(a_i^2 + b_i^2)^{1/2}e^{\sigma_i t}\cos(\omega_i t + \phi)$$

If the two poles s_i, s_i^* are located in the left-hand of the complex s plane, σ_i is negative and the response is an oscillatory exponentially decreasing function as illustrated Fig. B.5(b).

On the contrary, if the two poles are located in the right-hand half complex s plane, the response will be an oscillatory exponentially increasing function as illustrated Fig. B.6(b).

If $\sigma_i = 0$, the response to the unit-impulse function becomes

$$s(t) = 2(a_i^2 + b_i^2)^{1/2} \cos(\omega_i t + \phi_i)$$

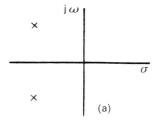
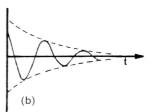

Fig. B.5   (a) Pair of complex conjugate poles whose real part is negative. (b) Response: damped oscillatory function.

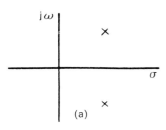
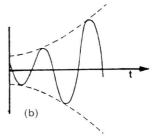

Fig. B.6   (a) Pair of complex conjugate poles whose real part is positive. (b) Response: oscillatory increasing impulse.

whose plot is represented in Fig. B.7(b). Such a response corresponds to the stability limit.

Note. To avoid complications we assumed that the poles were of order 1. If their order is q, it can be demonstrated that they correspond to q terms proportional to

$$t^{q-1}e^{s_it}, t^{q-2}e^{s_it}, \ldots, e^{s_it}$$

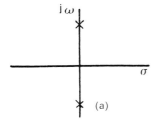
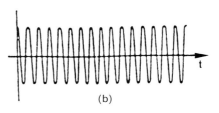

Fig. B.7   (a) Pair of complex conjugate poles on the imaginary axis. (b) Response: sinusoidal function.

B.3   STABILITY

B.3.1   Introduction

A system is said to be stable when its response to the unit-impulse function is stationary. As has been shown in the preceding sections, a system is stable when all the poles of the transfer function $T(s)$ are located on the left-hand half of the complex s plane. Since this result was established by assuming that poles were simple, we may wonder whether this result is also true if they are multiple. In that case the response terms are proportional to

$$t^{q-1}e^{s_i t}, t^{q-2}e^{s_i t}, ..., e^{s_i t}$$

Therefore, if $s_i = 0$, these terms approach 0 when t approaches 0 and the system is not stable. When s_i is simple and $\sigma_i = 0$, the response is at the threshold stability. Thus, to ensure stability of the complex conjugate poles the condition $\sigma_i < 0$ must be fulfilled.

A system is stable in any case if, and only if, the real part of the poles is negative.

B.3.2   Conditions ensuring stability

The block diagram of a feedback system in the time domain is illustrated in Fig. A.5. Therefore, the excitation and the response are functions of time.

If the system is studied in the frequency domain, we should replace the variables as follows:

$$e(t) \rightarrow E(s)$$
$$s(t) \rightarrow S(s)$$
$$g(t) \rightarrow G(s)$$
$$h(t) \rightarrow H(s)$$

The block diagram of the feedback system in the frequency domain becomes as

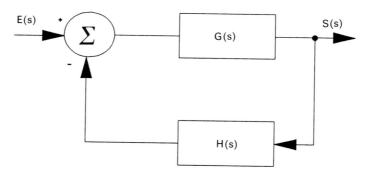

Fig. B.8   Feedback system block diagram in the frequency domain.

illustrated in Fig. B.8. From this diagram we deduce

$$[E(s) - S(s)H(s)]G(s) = S(s)$$

giving the so-called closed-loop transfer function:

$$T(s) = \frac{S(s)}{E(s)} = \frac{G(s)}{1 + H(s)G(s)}$$

The expression $H(s)G(s)$ is called the open-loop transfer function and it will be designated by $T'(p)$.

The transfer function $T(s)$ has no pole at the origin on the complex s plane.

We showed that a system is stable if, and only if, the roots of the characteristic equation of its transfer function $T(s)$ have their real part negative. In other words, the system is only stable if the equation

$$1 + G(s)H(s) = 0$$

with

$$1 + T'(s) = 0$$

has no roots with a positive real part.

B.3.3   Stability criterion

(a)   Routh–Hurwitz's criterion

A polynomial of the complex variable with real coefficients whose roots have a negative real part is called a Hurwitz polynomial. Therefore, its roots are located in the left-hand half of the s plane. Thus, if the characteristic equation of a feedback system is Hurwitz polynomial, the system is stable.

Consider the following equation which may be the characteristic equation of a feedback system:

$$1 + T'(s) = s^n + \alpha_1 s^{n-1} + \alpha_2 s^{n-2} + \cdots + \alpha_n$$

According to Routh's criterion it is possible to detect whether the roots have positive real parts by inspecting the coefficients of the polynomial.

Let us consider a particular case, namely a polynomial of the fifth order, and let us apply the Routh's criterion. Although the application is considered in a particular case it is valid as long as the polynomial is of the Hurwitz type.

The preceding equation is then written

$$\alpha_0 s^5 + \alpha_1 s^4 + \alpha_2 s^3 + \alpha_3 s^2 + \alpha_4 s^1 + \alpha_5$$

Let us construct Routh's table

s^5	α_0	α_2	α_4	0
s^4	α_1	α_3	α_5	

$$s^3 \quad B_1 \quad B_3$$
$$s^2 \quad C_1 \quad C_3$$
$$s^1 \quad D_1$$
$$s^0 \quad E_1$$

whose elements are related according to the following formulas:

$$B_1 = \frac{\alpha_1 \alpha_2 - \alpha_3 \alpha_0}{\alpha_1}$$

$$B_3 = \frac{\alpha_1 \alpha_4 - \alpha_5 \alpha_0}{\alpha_1}$$

$$C_1 = \frac{B_1 \alpha_3 - \alpha_1 B_3}{B_1}$$

$$C_3 = \frac{B_1 \alpha_5 - 0}{B_1} = \alpha_5$$

$$D_1 = \frac{C_1 B_3 - B_1 C_3}{C_1}$$

$$E_1 = \frac{D_1 C_3 - 0}{D_1} = C_3 = \alpha_5$$

The criterion is as follows: if all the coefficients of the second column of Routh's table are positive the roots of the polynomial have a negative real part.

Let us apply Routh's criterion to the following polynomial of the third degree:

$$s^3 + \alpha_1 s^2 + \alpha_2 s + \alpha_3 = 0$$

We construct the table

$$s^3 \quad 1 \quad \alpha_2 \quad 0$$
$$s^2 \quad \alpha_1 \quad \alpha_3$$
$$s^1 \quad B_1 \quad 0$$
$$s^0 \quad C_1$$

with

$$B_1 = \frac{\alpha_1 \alpha_2 - \alpha_3}{\alpha_1}$$

$$C_1 = \frac{B_1 \alpha_3 - \alpha_1 \times 0}{B_1} = \alpha_3$$

Therefore, for the system to be stable we should have

$$\alpha_1 > 0, \qquad \alpha_1 \alpha_2 - \alpha_3 > 0, \qquad \alpha_3 > 0$$

If there are n sign changes among the coefficients of the second column of Routh's, the equation has n roots located on the right-hand half of the complex s plan.

If all the coefficients of a row are equal to zero the equation has pure imaginary conjugate roots. In such a case the system is at the threshold of instability.

(b)   Evans root loci

Consider the characteristic equation $1 + G(s)H(s) = 0$, where $G(s)$ and $H(s)$ may be written

$$G(s) = k_1 \frac{P_1(s)}{Q_1(s)}$$

$$H(s) = k_2 \frac{P_2(s)}{Q_2(s)}$$

where k_1 and k_2 are two constants for a given system.

$P_1(s)$, $Q_1(s)$, $P_2(s)$ and $Q_2(s)$ are polynomials. If we consider $k_1 k_2 = k_T$ as a parameter that can take any value from 0 to infinity, then the roots will describe in the complex s plane the root loci. The roots are the poles of the closed-loop transfer function.

It has been shown that the stability of a feedback system could be deduced from the location of the poles of the closed-loop transfer function in the s plane, since the transfer function of a system at rest is the Laplace transform response to a unit-impulse function.

From the root loci, we can determine whether the system is stable or not, for a given value of k_T.

Let us consider the closed-loop transfer function

$$T(s) = \frac{b_m s^m + b_{m-1} s^{m-1} + \cdots + b_1 s + b_0}{a_n s^n + a_{n-1} s^{n-1} + \cdots + a_1 s + a_0}$$

and let us evaluate the roots of its denominator which are dependent on k_T:

$$a_n s^n + a_{n-1} s^{n-1} + \cdots + a_1 s + a_0 = 0$$

If the characteristic equation is a polynomial whose degree is less than 3 the root loci may be determined by a simple calculation. If third-degree (or greater) polynomials are involved manual calculations become cumbersome. Nevertheless, it is possible with a pocket calculator or a personal computer to calculate the roots for different values of k_T and to locate them in the s plane. If a large number of values of k_T are used, the number of roots is sufficient for us to join them in a continuous curve.

The plotting of the loci can be made easier by using the Evans method which provides a graphical technique for determining the roots of the characteristic equation of a feedback system by means of the poles and zeros of the open-loop transfer function $T'(s)$.

In order to avoid some confusion, the name 'roots' will be reserved for the poles of the closed-loop transfer function. The names 'poles' and 'zeros' will be used in connection with the open-loop transfer function.

The transfer function $T'(s)$ can be expressed as the quotient of two polynomials, that is to say

$$T'(s) = \frac{B_q \, s + (B_{q-1}/B_q)s^{q-1} + (B_{q-2}/B_q)s^{q-2} + \cdots + (B_1/B_q)s + B_0/B_q}{A_r \, s^r + (A_{r-1}/A_r)s^{r-1} + (A_{r-2}/A_r)s^{r-2} + \cdots + (A_1/A_r)s + A_0/A_r}$$

with $q < r$.

Setting $B_q/A_r = k_{T'}$ and substituting it in the preceding equation, we obtain

$$T'(s) = k_{T'} \frac{s^q + (B_{q-1}/B_q)s^{q-1} + (B_{q-2}/B_q)s^{q-2} + \cdots + (B_1/B_q)s + B_0/B_q}{s^r + (A_{r-1}/A_r)s^{r-1} + (A_{r-2}/A_r)s^{r-2} + \cdots + (A_1/A_r)s + A_0/A_r}$$

with $q < r$, which can be re-written as follows:

$$T'(s) = k_{T'} \frac{N(s)}{D(s)} \tag{B.1}$$

However, since

$$T(s) = \frac{G(s)}{1 + H(s)G(s)} = \frac{G(s)}{1 + T'(s)}$$

$$= \frac{G(s)}{1 + k_T N(s)/D(s)} = \frac{D(s)G(s)}{D(s) + k_{T'} N(s)}$$

the root loci are determined by the following equation:

$$D(s) + k_{T'} N(s) = 0 \tag{B.2}$$

A point M belongs to the root loci if its coordinates $s = \sigma + j\omega$ fulfil the preceding equation.

Evans rules for constructing the root loci

RULE 1

The branches of the root locus start at the poles of the open-loop transfer function where $k_{T'} = 0$ and terminate on the zeros of the same function where $k_{T'} = \infty$.

As a matter of fact, when $k_{T'} = 0$ equation (B.2) reduces to

$$D(s) = 0$$

whose roots are the poles of the open-loop transfer function.

When $k_{T'}$ approaches infinity, equation (B.2) may be written as follows:

$$\frac{D(s)}{k_{T'}} + N(s) = 0$$

Thus

$$N(s) = 0$$

and its roots are the zeros of the open-loop transfer function.

RULE 2
This is related to the phase and magnitude conditions. A point M_1 belongs to the locus if its coordinate $s_1 = \sigma_1 + j\omega_1$ is a root of the following equation:

$$T'(s) = -1 \tag{B.3}$$

Since $T'(s)$ is a complex number, it can be expressed as follows:

$$|T'(s)|e^{j\phi}$$

For a point M_1 to fulfil equation (B.3) it is necessary that

$$|T'(s)| = 1$$
$$\phi = (2k_0 + 1)\pi$$

RULE 3
The branches of the root locus are symmetrical with respect to the real axis. The coefficients of the polynomials being real, complex poles and zeros always occur in conjugate pairs.

RULE 4
The number of branches of the root locus is equal to the number of poles of the open-loop transfer function. This is due to equation (B.2), because the degree of the polynomial $N(s)$.

RULE 5
The branches of the root locus become asymptotic to straight lines for s approaching infinity that make angles of

$$\frac{(2k_0 + 1)\pi}{q - r}$$

As a matter of fact, when s approaches infinity, equation (B.1) becomes

$$T'(s) = \frac{B_q}{A_r}s^{q-r} = k_{T'}s^{q-r}$$

which can be re-written

$$T'(s) = |k_{T'}s^{q-r}|e^{j\phi}$$

However, since

$$T'(s) = -1$$

we obtain

$$|k_{T'}s^{q-r}| = 1$$
$$\phi = (2k_0 + 1)\pi$$

whence

$$T'(s) = |k_{T'}s^{q-r}|e^{(2k_0+1)\pi}$$

Extracting the $(q - r)$th root, we find the phase condition

$$\frac{(2k_0 + 1)\pi}{q - r} = -\frac{(2k_0 + 1)\pi}{r - q}$$
$$r \geqslant q$$

For instance, if $q = 1$ and $r = 4$ the angles of the asymptotes are $-60°$, $-180°$ and $-300°$ or $60°$.

RULE 6
The asymptotes meet the real axis in a point whose abscissa is

$$\sigma_0 = \frac{\displaystyle\sum_{j=1}^{r} s_j - \sum_{i=1}^{q} z_i}{r - q}$$

Poles and zeros being those of the open-loop transfer function, we write $T'(s)$ in the following form:

$$T'(s) = h\frac{(s - z_1)(s - z_2)\cdots(s - z_q)}{(s - s_1)(s - s_2)\cdots(s - s_r)}$$
$$= h\frac{s^q - (z_1 + z_2 + \cdots + z_q)s^{q-1} + \cdots + D_0}{s^r - (s_1 + s_2 + \cdots + s_r)s^{r-1} + \cdots + C_0}$$

Next we set

$$D_{q-1} = -(z_1 + z_2 + \cdots + z_q)$$
$$C_{r-1} = -(s_1 + s_2 + \cdots + s_r)$$

and substitution of this in the previous equation yields

$$T'(s) = h\frac{s^q + D_{q-1}s^{q-1} + \cdots + D_0}{s^r + C_{r-1}s^{r-1} + \cdots + C_0}$$

Next, dividing the numerator polynomial by the denominator polynomial, we obtain

$$T'(s) = \frac{h}{s^{r-q}(D_{q-1} - C_{r-1})s^{r-q-1} + \cdots}$$

and in order to fulfil the condition $|T'(s)| = -1$,

$$s^{r-q} + (D_{q-1} - C_{r-1})s^{r-q-1} = -h \tag{B.4}$$

Recalling the binomial development

$$(x + y)^n = x^n + nx^{n-1}y + \cdots \tag{B.5}$$

and then identifying the terms of equations (B.4) and (B.5), we obtain

$$x^n = s^{r-q}$$
$$ny = D_{q-1} - C_{r-1}$$

Thus

$$n = r - q$$
$$y = \frac{D_{q-1} - C_{r-1}}{r - q}$$

and

$$s^{r-q} + (D_{q-1} - C_{r-1})s^{r-q-1} = \left(s + \frac{D_{q-1} - C_{r-1}}{r - q} \right)^{r-q} = -h$$

from which we have, when $h = 0$

$$s = \sigma_0 = -\frac{D_{q-1} - C_{r-1}}{r - q}$$

Thus, the asymptotes meet at a point whose abscissa is determined by the relationship

$$\frac{\sum \text{poles} - \sum \text{zeros}}{(\text{number of poles}) - (\text{number of zeros})}$$

Let us remark that $h = k_{T'}$ and

$$k_T = k_{T'} \frac{\pi(-z_i)}{\pi(-s_j)}$$

RULE 7
On the real axis the branches of the root locus lie on alternate sections connecting the real poles and zeros of the open-loop transfer function, starting from the real pole or zero farthest to the right.

The root loci located on the real axis are determined by considering whether any point of the real axis belongs to the loci. Let P be a point of the loci on the real axis.

We can ignore the complex conjugate roots since they do not contribute to the angle condition. Also, the roots located to the left of P do not contribute. On the contrary, roots located to its left contribute to π or $-\pi$. Therefore, if the number of poles and zeros located to the right of P is an odd number, P belongs to the loci.

RULE 8
Any two real poles connected by a section of the root locus move towards each other as k_T increases, until they coincide; then they separate at right angles from the real axis forming a pair of complex conjugate roots.

(c)   Bode method

This consists of plotting, separately, the magnitude and the phase angle of the open-loop transfer function $T'(j\omega)$ versus the angular frequency ω.
    The magnitude is expressed in decibels according to the formula

$$U_{dB} = 20 \log |T'(j\omega)|$$

It is worth determining the cut-off angular frequency ω_c, defined as follows:

$$|T'(j\omega_c)| = 1$$

Expressed in decibels this becomes

$$20 \log |T'(j\omega_c)| = 0$$

It corresponds to the intersection of the Bode diagram with the horizontal 0 dB line.
    A feedback system is stable if the phase angle is above $-180°$ at the cut-off angular frequency.
    The margin phase Φ_M is defined as the difference between $180°$ and the phase corresponding to the cut-off angular frequency:

$$\Phi_M = 2\pi + \phi_{\omega_c}$$
$$\phi_{\omega_c} = \arg[T'(j\omega_c)]$$

Figure B.9 illustrates the Bode method.

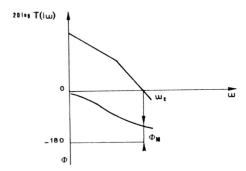

Fig. B.9   Bode method.

Appendix C The Fourier transform

C.1 DEFINITION

The Fourier transformation associates a given function $f(t)$ with a second function $F(j\omega)$ so that

$$F(j\omega) = \int_{-\infty}^{+\infty} f(t)e^{-j\omega t}\,dt$$

and the inverse Fourier transform is defined as

$$f(t) = \frac{1}{2\pi}\int_{-\infty}^{+\infty} F(j\omega)e^{j\omega t}\,d\omega$$

C.2 PARSEVAL'S THEOREM

Let us evaluate the integral of the square of $f(t)$; we find

$$\int_{-\infty}^{+\infty} f^2(t)\,dt = \int_{-\infty}^{+\infty} f(t)\,dt\,\frac{1}{2\pi}\int_{-\infty}^{+\infty} F(j\omega)e^{j\omega t}\,d\omega$$

Permuting, we obtain

$$\int_{-\infty}^{+\infty} f^2(t)\,dt = \frac{1}{2\pi}\int_{-\infty}^{+\infty} F(-j\omega)F(j\omega)\,d\omega = \int_{-\infty}^{+\infty} |F(j\omega)|^2\,df$$

where $f = \omega/2\pi$.

C.3 DUHAMEL'S THEOREM

Consider a non-varying linear system whose transfer function is $H(j\omega)$ and let us apply to its input a signal $x(t)$. According to the inverse Fourier transform, we have

$$x(t) = \frac{1}{2\pi}\int_{-\infty}^{+\infty} X(j\omega)e^{j\omega t}\,dt$$

In the following relations the system responses to the signals appearing in the integral are represented:

$$e^{j\omega t} \rightarrow H(j\omega)e^{j\omega t}$$

$$X(j\omega)e^{j\omega t} \rightarrow X(j\omega)H(j\omega)e^{j\omega t}$$

$$\frac{1}{2\pi}\int_{-\infty}^{+\infty} X(j\omega)e^{j\omega t}\,d\omega \rightarrow \frac{1}{2\pi}\int_{-\infty}^{+\infty} X(j\omega)H(j\omega)e^{j\omega t}\,d\omega$$

$$x(t) \rightarrow y(t)$$

The last but one relation shows that the inverse Fourier transform of the output signal $y(t)$ is equal to the product of the Fourier transform of the input signal $X(j\omega)$ by the Fourier transform of the unit-impulse response $H(j\omega)$: this theorem is attributed to Duhamel.

References

1. Rohde, U. L. (1983) *Digital PLL Frequency Synthesizers*, Prentice-Hall, London.
2. Best, R. E. (1983) *Phase Locked Loops, Theory, Design and Applications*, McGraw-Hill, New York.
3. Gardner, F. M. (1981) *Phaselock Techniques*, Wiley, New York.
4. Viterbi, A. J. (1966) *Principles of Coherent Communication*, McGraw-Hill, New York.
5. National Semiconductor (1973) *Linear Applications*, Application Note 46.
6. Blanchard, A. (1976) *Phaselock Loops*, Wiley, New York.
7. Gardner, F. M. (1980) Charge-pump phase-lock loops. *IEEE Trans. Commun.*, **28** (11), 1849–58.
8. Krauss, H. L. and Bostian, C. W. (1980) *Solid State Radio Engineering*, Wiley, New York.
9. de Bellescise, H. (1932) La réception synchrone, *Onde Electrique*, vol. 11.
10. Signetics (1974) *Digital, Linear, MOS Applications*, p. 6–41.

Further reading

de Carfort, F., Foulard, C. and Calvet, J. (1976) *Asservissements Linéaires et Continus*, Dunod Université.

Di Stefano, J., Stubberud, R. and Williams, J. (1974) *Feedback and Control Systems*, McGraw-Hill, New York.

Geiger, D. F. (1976) *Phaselock Loops for DC Motor Speed Control*, New York.

Legros, R. (1974) *Calcul Transformationnel*, Masson.

Girard, M. (1988) *Boucles à Verrouillage de Phase*, McGraw-Hill.

Hakim, S. S. (1966) *Feedback Circuit Analysis*, Iliffe, London.

Manassewitsch, V. (1976) *Frequency Synthesizers: Theory and Design*, Wiley, New York.

Index